EDITORI

This issue ranges from the US Navy's turn of the century *Arkansas* class monitors to the current dominance of the gas turbine in the technology of surface warship propulsion. It profiles two of the fastest, most powerful yet shortlived conventional destroyers ever built, *Mogador* and *Volta*, largely eclipsed by their smaller but better known *Fantasque* class predecessors (most of whom survived) and sets them alongside the numerous and mass-produced Japanese 'Kaibokan' escorts of the same era. It is fascinating to learn that the Imperial Japanese Navy or rather Mitsubishi Industries decided that this lowest priority ship should nevertheless be built to the highest standards. This policy of quality before quantity meant that the bloated seaborne Japanese Empire of 1942-43, even if her naval planners had paid the slightest attention to the ASW, could never have deployed in time the sheer numbers of convoy escorts (with trained ASW crews) needed to save her merchant shipping from massacre by the US submarine force in the Pacific.

What a contrast with the Atlantic at the same juncture where the Allied shipyards on both sides of the Atlantic were pouring out hundreds of cheap and far from ideal anti-submarine hulls to counteract the more concentrated threat of Hitler's U-boat arm. As Norman Friedman feelingly remarks in his article on US SSK ASW submarines, this was 'the last great ASW war', the experience of which guided the US Navy's ASW plans during the Cold War. It is incredible to read now that their 1948 prediction of the Soviet underwater threat in about 1960 was the little matter of 2000 submarines for which the West's most effective counter was going to be the construction of 970 hunter-killer boats.

We may take some comfort from this illustration of the fact that the worst case does not always arise. Furthermore the very same geographical constraints on Russian submarine deployment apply in 1984 just as surely as they did in 1948. What changed the equation was the naval revolution wrought by nuclear power. It is perhaps ironical that in the middle of all the fashionable concern with East-West nuclear *warheads* the atom in its largely forgotten role of underwater propulsion has immeasurably sustained the cause of deterrence and peace.

Just as on land the West can never hope, nor has it ever planned, to match the Warsaw Pact division, tank for tank, gun for gun or missile for missile so at sea it can be argued that the nuclear-powered submarine has, in both its missile-carrying and hunter-killer guises, saved the West from the crippling financial and perhaps politically impossible burden of furnishing the requisite non-nuclear naval forces. Nuclear submarines are expensive but they offer unmatchable endurance and mobility for a very small expenditure of manpower which is kept largely out of sight (of land) and mind.

It is the nuclear dimension above all that colours the fact that in terms of this fast diminishing twentieth century we are as far in time from the Battle of Leyte Gulf as its participants were from the Battle of Tsushima. This issue of *Warship* has a salutary assessment of the constant effect of wind and weather on the surface warship but the acknowledged if easily forgotten dreadnoughts of our time operate beneath the waves, their vulnerabilities seldom exposed to the world at large. They exert a silent dominance that has persisted now for more than two decades. Only five nations operate vessels of this type and in eloquent contrast with all the other outpourings of the arms trade these are not weapons for sale.

The continuing fuss in some quarters over the sinking of the Argentine cruiser *General Belgrano*, one is tempted to say, is partly a reflection of the *nuclear* submarine's awesome capabilities. The fact that a World War II ship was sunk with World War II torpedoes was of far less importance than it was done by a nuclear submarine which had stalked her prey for more than 30 hours. It was not even the first successful submarine torpedo attack since 1945 (that can be credited to the Pakistan/French built *Daphne*-class diesel boat *Hangor* which sank the Indian frigate *Khukri* with heavy loss of life in the Arabian Sea on 9 December 1971) but that brief British use of a weapon with latent power has had a lasting psychological impact on friend and foe alike.

The argument for nuclear submarines is very much a closed one involving as it does the most secret technical details of all in a sphere that is remoter to the layman than outer space. But the emphasis of Sir John Nott's 1981 White Paper 'The Way Ahead' on an ASW partnership of hunter-killer nuclear submarine and maritime patrol aircraft may only have been an extreme statement of what is already the daily reality of NATO deterrence. As such, however desirable more surface ships of all kinds would be for in and out of area tasks, the central strategic balance rests on the quality of a handful of high speed underwater ASW and missile platforms manned by specialist submariners.

Randal Gray

The Gas Turbine at Sea

by John M Maber

MGB 2009 on trials in Stokes Bay (Solent) during which she exceeded 34 knots. Engined with the Metropolitan-Vickers Gatric, the first gas turbine to see service at sea.

Popperfoto

The marine gas turbine is accepted today as a compact propulsion plant of proven reliability suited to the needs of medium and high powered warship installations either in a multiple unit configuration or in association with the diesel engine. Compared with conventional steam turbine machinery burning oil fuel, the modern aircraft-derived gas turbine reduces engine room manning and requires less onboard maintenance. It is also easier to replace with a new unit when a major overhaul is due.

RESEARCH BEFORE 1914
The idea of burning fuel in a gas generator and using the resultant combustion gases to drive a turbine wheel is by no means a recent concept and indeed numerous, although generally impractical, proposals were made in the course of the nineteenth century. In the event, it is probable that attention was first given to the development of a practical self-contained internal combustion turbine towards the end of the century by a German engineer, Dr Stolze, who in 1900 actually constructed and was able to demonstrate a working unit. Some six years later M Rene Armengaud converted a de Laval impulse steam turbine to operate on compressed air

mixed with metered quantities of petroleum vapour, the mixture being fired continuously by means of an incandescent platinum wire igniter. The useful output was about 30hp.

Inevitably, the designer came up against the problem of high gas temperature which was to prevent any substantial advance in practical gas turbine design until the 1940s when the needs of war engendered significant developments in the field of metallurgy. In Armengaud's machine combustion took place at about 1800° C and the combustion chamber was lined with carborundum (silicon carbide), a crystalline refractory material, but steam generated in a steam coil sited within this chamber mixed with the gaseous combustion products to bring the turbine inlet temperature down to about 400° C (762° F).

In addition to Armengaud's work in France, a sizeable effort was devoted to gas turbine development in Germany where in 1910 Holzwarth designed and built at the Thyssen works in Mulheim, with the help of Korting Brothers and the Brown-Boveri company, a vertical 1000hp constant volume internal combustion turbine directly coupled to a direct current generator mounted above the unit. In lieu of the continuous ignition principle of the Armengaud turbine, ignition in the Holzwarth machine was achieved through a spark generated by a high tension magneto. The hot gases produced passed to a two-stage Curtis impulse turbine and steam generated by otherwise waste exhaust heat was used to drive the turbo-compressor that supplied the combustion air. In fact, however, this 'waste' heat represented a major part of the theoretical output of the machine and in practice the useful power amounted to something like 160bhp only!

The gas turbine's potential as a possible marine propulsion unit was discussed, with particular reference to the Holzwarth design, in an article in *The Naval Annual* for 1913, but development work in Germany came to a halt following the outbreak of war in 1914. Trials were resumed in 1918, however, in the wake of interest shown by the Prussian State Railway administration and in the following year an order was placed for a 500hp traction unit coupled to a direct current generator. At about the same time renewed consideration was given to using an internal combustion turbine for marine propulsion and in December 1920 a Holzwarth unit arranged for mechanical transmission via reduction gearing was delivered for trials.

Like modern gas generators this marine unit had a number of equally spaced combustion chambers, in this case six, arranged around a horizontal shaft but as in earlier Holzwarth designs the centrifugal air compressor was driven by a steam turbine utilising the exhaust gas heat for steam generation. The design of a 500kw marine internal combustion turbine of this configuration was discussed and illustrated in *The Motor Ship* for May 1922 but at best the machine was regarded only as an uncertain rival for the well-proven geared steam turbine.

HMS *Grey Goose*, a former steam gunboat re-engined in 1952-54 with a pair of Rolls Royce RM60 turbines.
MoD

BRITISH DEVELOPMENT 1938-48

As matters turned out, the Holzwarth design's complexity, with its inefficient steam driven compressor and doubts about its material reliability in view of the high temperatures involved, militated against further practical marine gas turbine development for another 20 years. Between the wars, however, the Parsons Marine Steam Turbine Company in England, among others, did devote considerable effort to the development of an axial flow compressor and in 1938 this company built an experimental gas turbine incorporating an engine-driven compressor of axial flow design thus opening the way ahead for the later development of a compact self-contained gas generator.

Elsewhere the gas turbine was under development as an aircraft jet engine and in 1941 Frank Whittle (later Sir Frank Whittle) produced his first successful aero-engine prototype. In the meantime, research work continued on what was essentially an internal combustion version of the marine steam turbine since advantages were seen in its basic simplicity compared with the diesel engine and in the fact that it could be run on a wide range of fuels. Compared with the aircraft gas turbine, such machines were heavy and comparatively slow running although in fact this was not considered to be any great drawback. It was expected that engine life would equate to ship life, far exceeding an aircraft engine's and would require little onboard maintenance.

Apart from marine gas turbine design work stemming from a steam ancestry, with which Metropolitan-Vickers Ltd of Manchester were primarily associated, the Admiralty had not been slow in developing a propulsion unit based upon Sir Frank Whittle's pioneering work. The naval staff requirement was in fact twofold: first there was a demand for a compact high-powered, short

HMS *Bold Pathfinder* (MTB 5720), one of a pair of experimental prototype fast patrol boats engined with Metropolitan-Vickers G2 gas turbines in a 4-shaft CODAG arrangement.

Author's collection

life engine (of aircraft derived design) for high speed coastal craft; second, in the longer term, there was a need for a boost plant for the surface warship which spends the greater part of its operational time at sea at cruising or lower speeds. Thus, in 1943 a contract was placed, again with Metropolitan-Vickers Ltd, to develop a propulsion gas turbine based on Whittle's F2 aircraft jet engine. The marine engine required the addition of an output power turbine in the jet pipe and was to burn diesel oil rather than the kerosene (paraffin) burned in the aircraft application. Shore trials were completed in 1946 in the wake of the solution to a number of design problems and in the following year an engine of this type, known by this time as the Gatric, was installed in place of the centre-line Packard Merlin piston engine (aviation fuel) in *MGB 2009*, a three-shaft 115-ton wartime built motor gunboat of Camper & Nicholson

design. A successful series of trials followed, extending over three years, and this engine, the first gas turbine in service at sea, is now preserved in the Science Museum, London.

RN 'BOLD' CLASS 1950s TRIALS
Towards the end of 1948 a further contract was placed with Metropolitan-Vickers for the development of a larger marine engine based upon the Beryl aircraft turbine. Four gas turbines of this type, known as the G2, were built for installation as boost units to run in parallel with ex-German Mercedes Benz MB 518 diesel engines at high speeds in a four-shaft arrangement for a pair of prototype fast patrol boats to be named *Bold Pathfinder* and *Bold Pioneer*. Built respectively by Vospers of Portsmouth and J Samuel White of Cowes, these two craft were intended to assess the relative merits of round bilge and hard chine construction. The 2500hp diesel engines, which were direct reversing and thus used for manoeuvring, drove the inner shafts while the gas turbines drove the outer shafts. No clutches were provided and the wing shafts with the power turbine rotors were trailed at cruising or manoeuvring speeds.

Sea trials with HMS *Bold Pioneer* started late in 1951 but many teething troubles were encountered although much was learned and the G2 engine added considerably to the sum total of practical marine gas turbine propulsion. In particular, there were no air intake filters and the gas generator suffered from the build up of salt deposits on the compressor blading such that, in other than low sea states, water washing was necessary at intervals of about 20 minutes. *Bold Pathfinder* followed in 1953. After these trials a G2 Mk II engine was developed which, although never fitted in any vessel for the Royal Navy, was purchased by the US Navy and installed in a PT boat for trials. A later, more robust, G4 development was similarly overtaken by events in so far as the RN was concerned but did go to sea in the 197-ton Italian motor gunboats *Lampo* and *Baleno* completed in 1963-65.

COSAG 1950s AND 1960s
In the development of an engine for larger warships, early work centred on a turbine designed and built by the English Electric Co at Rugby. This 6500bhp EL60A turbine was intended to replace one of the steam sets in the twin screw turbo-electric frigate *Hotham*, a US-built vessel of the 'Captains' class selected in view of the comparative ease with which the power turbine drive could be matched to the electric transmission. In the event, manufacturing difficulties delayed development and it was not until late in 1951 that the gas turbine set was delivered for shore trials. By this time it was already becoming apparent that there was little future for an

HMS *Exmouth*, the world's first all gas turbine major warship in which a Perseus/Olympus COGOG arrangement replaced the original steam plant.

Author's collection

engine of this type based on steam turbine practice for main propulsion duty and plans for *Hotham*'s conversion were abandoned.

This was not to say, however, that no future was seen for the long life steam turbine derived boost unit and design work, which continued at Metropolitan-Vickers (subsequently part of AEI Ltd), in association with the Admiralty, resulted eventually in the development of the G6. This 7500bhp gas turbine was for installation as part of the combined steam and gas turbine (COSAG) propulsion packages in the Type 81 'Tribal' class frigates and the Seaslug-armed guided missile destroyers of the 'County' class that entered service during the early 1960s. In both classes the gearing was arranged so that the gas turbine drive could not only boost the steam plant for full speed, ahead only, but also could be employed, independently, for manoeurvring ahead and astern thus permitting a quick getaway of the ship from cold. Once again limited teething troubles were experienced, but the plant proved itself and pointed the way to the future although in fact the G6 was to be the last of the heavy, comparatively slow-running and low-powered marine gas turbines derived from the steam age. Franco Tosi built G6 turbines in a twin-screw combined diesel and gas (CODAG) arrangement were chosen also in the 1960s for the ageing Italian destroyer *San Giorgio* (ex-*Pompeo Magno*), launched in 1941 but completely rebuilt in 1963-65 as a cadet training ship, and for the 2689-ton frigates *Alpino* and *Carabiniere* completed in 1968.

BRITISH ALL-GAS TURBINE PROPULSION
In the meantime, Messrs Rolls Royce, in association with the Admiralty, had developed for fast attack craft a lightweight if complex engine designated the RM60

HMS *Devonshire*, the first of the COSAG engined 'County' class destroyers. Completed in 1962, she was equipped with four AEI G6 boost turbines, each of 7500bhp.
Author's collection

which although not aircraft derived did owe its origins to aero-engine design expertise. Following extensive shore trials two of these units, rated at 5400bhp, were installed in the former steam gunboat *Grey Goose* (ex-*SGB 9*), the first warship in any navy to be powered entirely by gas turbines. HMS *Grey Goose* ran successfully for some four years (1952-55) building up an impressive total of engine running hours although very expensive in fuel. In the event, however, development of the sophisticated RM60 was abandoned in favour of the naval Proteus turbine developed by Bristol Aero Engines for fast craft.

The Bristol Proteus first ran in January 1947 and consideration for its development as a marine engine followed in 1954 when Vosper of Portsmouth was given a contract to undertake a design study for a new class of fast patrol boats (FPB). Various engine combinations and arrangements were investigated but eventually the choice fell on a three-shaft configuration with three Proteus gas turbines each rated at 3500bhp. Orders for two boats, to be known as the 'Brave' class, went to Vospers in March 1956, but subsequent reappraisal of the Royal Navy's role within NATO led to the effective abandonment of Britain's coastal forces although in fact when the end came in 1957 it was agreed that the two 'Braves' should be completed for use in a training role.

One of the greatest success stories to date in the marine gas turbine field has been this development of the Bristol (Rolls Royce from 1967) Proteus. Its debut at sea came in the FPB *Brave Borderer* during 1958. A compact engine, it had been designed to power propeller-driven aircraft and thus incorporated a power turbine at the outset. No great modification was required other than some change of materials and redesign of the fuel system to enable the engine to run on diesel oil. The 'Braves' were followed by a series of similar Proteus-engined hard chine hulled craft for the Danish, Malaysian, Brunei, Libyan and West German navies. The Swedish 'Spica' class MTBs, too, employed a similar machinery configuration. Proteus has also been fitted in a variety of British, US and Italian-designed hovercraft and hydrofoils. Two Proteus turbines, uprated to 4250bhp, were fitted as cruise engines in the converted Type 14 frigate HMS *Exmouth* as the Royal Navy's, and indeed the world's, first operational all gas turbine major warship which recommissioned for service in June 1968.

The high speed plant in the *Exmouth* COGOG (combined gas or gas) conversion comprised a single Bristol Siddley (later Rolls Royce) Olympus TM1A module. Although rated at 22,500bhp it could not be used at its full output because the existing hull design restricted the maximum to 15,000shp. Similar engines have been fitted, however, in a number of frigates of commercial design built for the Brazilian, Iranian, Malaysian and Thai navies by the Vosper-Thornycroft, Vickers and Yarrow companies, and also as the boost plant in the COSAG-engined guided missile destroyer HMS *Bristol*. The Olympus TM1A gas generator was derived from the aircraft turbojet employed in the supersonic transport Concorde redesigned to burn diesel fuel instead of kerosene and exhausting into a single-stage power turbine of robust 'ship life' design to drive the gearbox input shaft.

Marine gas turbine progress was not confined to Britain of course and during the 1950s, in both the United States and France, successful units were developed to the trial installation stage, of both the turbine and an opposed piston gas generator type. Elsewhere in Europe the Brown-Boveri company of Mannheim, again active in the gas turbine field, developed on behalf of the Federal German *Bundesmarine* a 12,000bhp gas turbine for the 2750-ton twin screw CODAG *Köln* class frigates, the first of which commissioned for service in April 1961. At about the same time the first units of the 1150-ton CODAG-engined 'Petya I' class escort vessels joined the Soviet Fleet. In these triple screw craft the centre shaft is driven by a pair of 3000bhp diesel engines while the wing shafts, which are trailed at crusing speeds up to 16-18 knots, are driven by 15,000bhp gas turbines.

The development of such plant in the United States for active fleet duty lagged somewhat behind that achieved for the European navies. Not until August 1966 did the first CODAG-powered patrol gunboats of the US Navy's *Asheville* class commission for service. These 245-ton (full load) twin screw craft were engined with a pair of 875bhp Cummins diesels and a single aircraft-derived General Electric LM1500 gas turbine of 14,000shp.

It must be borne in mind of course that marine gas turbine operating cycle and its environmental conditions are vastly different from those applying to the aircraft engine. The marine unit must be capable of running continuously at near full power day after day, while the problems of salt and water ingestion necessitate careful design of the air intake system. Additionally there is the problem of waste heat disposal which in the equivalent steam plant is transferred to the condenser circulating water and is thus conveniently discharged into the sea. In a marine gas turbine plant the hot exhaust goes from the power turbine pass via the uptakes to atmosphere necessitating attention to design detail to keep the gases clear of the ship's structure and the employment of high cost alloy steels for the uptake system. In early commerical marine installations, attempts were made to utilise the waste heat but the heat exhanger weight and size, necessarily sited high in the ship, destroyed any advantage that might have been gained while its very presence in the exhaust path resulted in a significant reduction in engine output.

COGOG TODAY

HMS *Bristol*, the last steam driven (COSAG) warship for the Royal Navy, entered service a decade ago and, in her wake, the present generation of missile armed destroyers (Type 42) and frigates (Type 22), together with the older Type 21 frigates, is engined with the uprated

HMS *Birmingham*, a Seadart armed Type 42 destroyer (on contractor's 1976 sea trials) fitted with the two-shaft Tyne/Olympus package.
MoD

Starboard side of the gearbox of the Metropolitan-Vickers Gatric gas turbine that can now be seen in the Science Museum, London.

Popperfoto

(28,000bhp) Olympus TM3B gas turbine for high speed and a naval Rolls Royce Tyne (4250bhp), the RM1A, for the low speed range in a twin-shaft COGOG arrangement with controllable pitch propellers. In all these vessels the layout of the machinery spaces has been designed for ease of engine exchange when major overhauls become due thus to minimise ship downtime and, in turn, to ensure maximum availability. Both these engines were successfully changed at sea by repair ships in the aftermath of the Falklands War. A similar Olympus/Tyne COGOG configuration is employed in contemporary Dutch destroyers and frigates, respectively of the *Tromp* and *Kortenaer* classes. Two further Type 42 destroyers, for the Argentine Navy, were delivered in 1976/81, one built at Barrow and the other built locally in the Rio Santiago Navy Yard, in addition to which Olympus and Tyne propulsion modules have been supplied for four 2900-ton twin screw COGOG destroyers (*Almirante Brown* class) built for that same navy by Blohm & Voss at Hamburg. In the case of the 19,500-ton *Invincible* class VSTOL carriers (CVS) a twin-shaft arrangement with four Olympus TM3B driving fixed pitch propellers is employed.

The Soviet Navy, too, following experience gained with the 'Petya' classes, adopted gas turbine propulsion extensively, initially for the new generation destroyers/frigates of the 1960s and 1970s such as the 'Kashin' and 'Krivak' classes and, more recently, for the heavily armed cruisers of the 9800-ton 'Kara' class (4 engines driving 2 shafts). The latter's successor class, the 'Krasinas', beginning with *Slava* in mid-1983, are similarly equipped.

As mentioned above, the United States lagged behind

in marine gas turbine development and not until 1970 did the US Navy place an order with Litton Industries for a class of 7800-ton missile armed destroyers engined on two shafts with four General Electric LM2500 turbines, each of about 20,000bhp. The gas generator is derived from the TF39 turbofan aircraft engine and, as in the case of the Royal Navy, this type of plant has been adopted because of its compact design, reduced operator and onboard maintenance demands compared with the equivalent steam plant, rapid cold start capability and the ease of unit exchange. The lead ship of the class, USS *Spruance*, first commissioned in September 1975 and the delivery of 31 vessels has now been completed. Two General Electric units of the same type power the smaller frigates of the *Oliver Hazard Perry* class, although in this case reliance on a single shaft COGAG arrangement with two large engines to cope with the total power range would appear to lack the flexibility of the Royal Navy's Olympus/Tyne system.

In the late 1960s, during the course of development of the Olympus/Tyne propulsion package, a need was seen for an engine of medium output, since at other than the upper sector of its power range the Olympus is relatively inefficient. This requirement stemmed from the advent of sonars capable of being employed effectively at greater speeds than hitherto. In 1972 the Ministry of Defence placed a feasibility study contract with Rolls Royce for a naval version of the well-proven Spey turbofan engine. The most powerful engine in the Spey range, the TF41, was chosen for this exercise and in 1977 a development contract followed for the design and construction of a 12.5 megawatt (16,750bhp) unit, known by this time as the SM1A. The gas generator is of twin spool design with the low pressure and high pressure compressors independently driven by their own two-stage turbines. They are thus able to run at their optimum speeds having a much improved fuel economy compared with that possible in the earlier generation of engines. The module incorporates a two-stage power turbine of 'ship life' design.

Development of what has the makings of a very successful unit preceded any committment to a specific ship, but the Spey SM1A is now to be fitted, together with an uprated Tyne, the 5340bhp RM1C, in the Batch 3 Type 22 frigate and as a boost unit in association with a diesel-electric cruise drive for the Type 23 quiet running frigate, details of which were announced late in 1983. In the meantime a twin-screw Spey SM1A/Olympus TM3B COGOG propulsion plant has been specified by the Japanese Maritime Self Defence Force for three 4500-ton destroyers, the first of which was launched by Mitsubishi at Nagasaki in May 1983.

Today the majority of warships in the destroyer and frigate categories are gas turbine powered, either by a COGOG or COGAG (combined gas turbine and gas turbine) plant, or by employing diesel cruise engines with gas turbines for higher speeds in a CODOG configuration, or alternatively with a boost turbine in a CODAG arrangement. Much the largest gas turbine engined warships are the 19,800-ton *Invincible* class VSTOL carriers, but the US Navy is currently building a series of 8910-ton missile armed cruisers, known as the

HMS *Ardent* in June 1977, a Tyne/Olympus COGOG engined Type 21 frigate. She was lost during the Falklands War.
Author's collection

Ticonderoga class, engined on two shafts like the *Spruance* class with four General Electric LM2500 turbines. Meanwhile the Italian Navy has specified the same engine fit, manufactured under licence by Fiat, for the 13,250-ton light aircraft carrier *Giuseppe Garibaldi* now under construction by Italcantieri at Monfalcone.

The Royal Navy apart, Rolls Royce aircraft derived gas turbines are installed as propulsion engines in the

HMS *Battleaxe*, a Tyne/Olympus engined Type 22 frigate. Note the massive gas turbine uptakes.
Author's collection

warships of no fewer than 19 navies. And if one takes into consideration the fit of other makes of engine, including General Electric of USA, Pratt & Witney (USA), GE-Fiat (Italy) and those of Russian origin, it is clear that the gas turbine is today's preferred powerplant for fast warships. The gas turbine does present problems for the naval architect, however, in that it does not like the ingestion of salt laden spray while the fact that all the waste heat is exhausted to atmosphere makes necessary very large uptakes. Again, the radiated heat itself presents an attractive target for heat-seeking missiles. Against this must be set the advantages enumerated at the beginning of this article and it is likely that the gas turbine powerplant will continue to be favoured for fast, medium-sized craft of the destroyer/frigate classes for the foreseeable future.

WARSHIP WINGS

No.9 Sea Harrier

by Roger Chesneau

While it is stretching things to claim that the remarkable Harrier family of aircraft has revolutionised fixed-wing naval aviation, it cannot be denied that its development has had a significant impact on the ability of navies to project carrier-based air power. The explosive growth in carrier aircraft size and weight during the postwar years, dictated by ever-increasing speeds, range, carrying capability and electronics complexity, has left the United States and, probably, the Soviet Union as the only nations able, or perhaps willing, to afford the vast and expensive ships necessary to operate a comprehen-

sive range of types. However, by addressing such questions as take-off distance, and obviating the need for catapults and, indeed, arrester gear, V/STOL (Vertical/Short Take-Off and Landing) aircraft strike deeply at several major factors contributing to the size and cost of modern fleet carriers.

It is not proposed here to recount the Harrier development story nor to relate the events of the spring and early summer of 1982, when the aircraft, confounding its not inconsiderable numbers of critics, proved itself during the 45 combat days of the Falklands War as a highly effective air defence, strike and reconnaissance fighter; these topics have been covered in depth by numerous publications already. Rather, we might attempt to outline some aspects of the Harrier's versatility and its impact on parent ships.

V/STOL AND THE FLIGHT DECK

Theoretically, V/STOL requires a platform only a little more generous in overall dimensions than those of the aircraft itself, but in practice VTO (Vertical Take-Off) imposes several limitations on the machine's performance. For example, lift is provided exclusively by the thrust of the powerplant, thus placing weight restrictions (generally affecting the variables, ie armament payload and/or fuel) on the airframe; as a result, range or offensive capability (or both) are penalised. Moreover, VTO is inherently a fuel-thirsty manoeuvre. At a different level, little safety margin is available to a pilot engaged in VTO in the event of crisis, such as engine failure.

Hence STO (Short Take-Off) rather than VTO is the rule for Harrier operations at sea, although landings are generally conducted in the vertical mode, at least in the Royal Navy. STO is of course enhanced via the well-known 'ski-jump' technique (invented by Lt-Cdr D R Taylor in 1978), which conveniently tackles the problems mentioned above by giving the departing aircraft a semi-ballistic trajectory and allowing the wings to generate lift, as they do in conventional take-off rolls. Ski-jump STO gives the Sea Harrier 2000lb more payload than ordinary STO. In fact, a further benefit is that short rolling take-offs via ski-jumps actually increase the tempo of the flight-deck cycle, a typical operating figure being one machine every 15-20 seconds. It is no exaggeration to say that the ski-jump device alone made possible the Harrier operations in the South Atlantic.

Although V/STOL has immense benefits with regard to take-off roll and renders superfluous the elaborate launching and recovery equipment necessary to operate conventional aircraft, ship impact in other respects is modified less significantly. Thus V/STOL confers few advantages insofar as stowage, hangar or flight deck, is concerned, other than in the sense that airframe weight,

Eight Sea Harriers of No 809 Squadron in formation 1982. This squadron was reformed between April and December for the Falklands War.
British Aerospace

Underside view of Sea Harrire ZA174, showing the arrangement of the jet nozzels and the large twin Aden 30mm gun pods beneath the fuselage. The doppler panel below the nose is clearly evident.
British Aerospace

A Sea Harrier lifts off from RNAS Yeovilton's land-based training ski-jump, 1980. The aircraft is finished in the original colour scheme of Extra Dark Sea Grey and White and is carrying Sea Eagle ASMs on the inboard pylons.
British Aerospace

and hence size, is limited by the thrust available from the preferred powerplant and consequently smaller aircraft occupy a relatively smaller space. But, static aircraft do, after all, consume a fixed volume, and such considerations as magazine and aviation fuel capacity are more intimately related to the number of machines in the air group, the fuel consumption and the range of those aircraft, and the number of operational flights each is expected to undertake, rather than to the method by which they leave or arrive on board the carrier. Onboard limitations can, however, partly be alleviated by the versatility of an airframe. If an air group comprises what is essentially a single aircraft type, fewer spares and weapons of less varieties will be needed, and the maintenance, in the form of both manpower and facilities, will take up less space on board than in a ship operating several types of aircraft. Furthermore, equipment such as lifts presumably makes fewer demands on designers if a wide variety of aircraft types does not need to be handled.

The Sea Harrier operates as a fighter, reconnaissance and strike aircraft (hence 'FRS') and its multi-role capability, decried by many as requiring too much of a compromise in aircraft design, has in this instance proven remarkably successful. It is worth remembering too that for the last 10 days of the Falklands War Sea Harriers and RAF Harriers operated from the improvised 285-year 'Sid's Strip' at Port San Carlos with an almost fourfold improvement in time on patrol. Such flexible

Close-up of the starboard wingtip, showing the RCV (Reaction Control Valve) duct, used for manoeuvring at very low speeds. Similar valves are fitted to the nose and tail of the aircraft. Note the lash-down lug on the outrigger wheel leg.
Linewrights Ltd

operation from a temporary land base is obviously not possible for conventional naval aircraft.

SCADS
The attraction of V/STOL in requiring only relatively basic flight deck facilities in order to operate modern, high-performance aircraft, has led to a large number of studies for austere carriers, many taking the form of readily convertible merchant ships. One current project, encouraged by the success of extemporary aircraft ferries deployed to the South Atlantic in 1982, is SCADS (Shipborne Containerised Air Defence System). Proposed by British Aerospace, it envisages a container ship fitted with a flight deck terminating in a ski-jump, plus a

Refuelling an 899 Sqn Sea Harrier, RNAS Yeovilton, August 1983. This and the preceding photograph are representative of a very large selection of Sea Harrier close-up views included in *Aeroguide 3: Sea Harrier*, recently published by Linewrights Ltd at £2.95.

Linewrights Ltd

Seawolf SAM system and a basic electronics (including ECM) suite. The air group would comprise six Sea Harriers plus a couple of Sea King AEW helicopters, accommodation and control facilities being provided during rapid conversion by means of standard containers already fitted out for the purpose. British Aerospace foresee a valuable role for SCADS particularly as a convoy protection vessel, with a viable anti-air and anti-surface component in the form of her aircraft. Doubtless an ASW role could also be conferred on the ship, given the appropriate equipment. The analogy with World War II escort carriers, and in particular with CAM/MAC-ships, is obvious.

SKYHOOK

More radical is a proposal to deploy and retrieve Sea Harrier aircraft by means of the Skyhook space-stabilised cranes. A ship so fitted would be able to 'catch' a hovering aircraft and either hold it for refuelling or bring it aboard for rearming, maintenance or stowage within a small hangar. The principle involved is the acquisition by the pilot of a 10 cubic ft 'box' wherein the crane, stabilised to cope with seas up to State 6, can locate by sensor a pick-up point on top of the aircraft's fuselage, following which the pilot could shut down.

SEA HARRIER FRS Mk I SPECIFICATION

Overall length	47ft 7in
Span	25ft 3in
Max height	12ft 2in
Wing area	201.1sq ft
Engine	One Rolls-Royce Pegasus 104 vectored-thrust turbofan, 21,500lb static thrust
Max speed	Probably in excess of 640kts
Combat radius	(Surface strike, no external fuel) 210nm
Weight	26,200lb max take-off; 16,900lb design VL
Weapons	(Typical air defence mode) 2 × 30mm Aden cannon, 2 × AIM-9L AAMs, 2 × 190gal drop tanks. Twin Sidewinders can be accommodated on each outboard pylon, and for the strike role 3 × 1000lb bombs, or 68mm SNEB rocket pods or ASMs (Martel, Harpoon, Sea Eagle) can be carried

Deployment uses the reverse procedure, the Harrier's unique hovering capabilities being utilised to stabilise the aircraft prior to uncoupling and departure. British Aerospace estimate that ships displacing as little as 3000 tons would be able to operate such a system, aircraft launch occupying about one minute and recovery twice that.

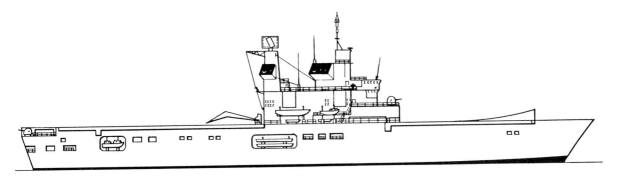

Vickers Shipbuilding drawing (issued July 1981) of a possible low-cost 'Sea Harrier Carrier' with ski-jump.

Vickers

Whether these schemes come to fruition is a matter of doubt; despite the Sea Harrier's proven success, there seems to be some reluctance on the part of navies to introduce them. Perhaps they are waiting for the emergence of Sea Harrier's *supersonic* successor – the radically different P1216 being developed by British Aerospace and McDonnell Douglas in the USA. However, recent reports of the Indian Navy increasing its Sea Harrier order from 8 to 20 aircraft and of the Italians seriously contemplating the purchase of a number of machines for deployment aboard their new carrier *Garibaldi* are perhaps the start of renewed interest. One thing is evident: the naval V/STOL story has only just begun.

Skyhook trials have included holding a Sea Harrier on station with a fixed reference point (in this instance a 50ft high fire ladder), using a basic parallax sight. Note that the aircraft demonstrating the concept here is an Indian Navy machine.

British Aerospace

TECHNICAL NOTE
It's rough out there

by D K Brown RCNC

The sea is rarely smooth, often rough and sometimes very rough indeed. The influence of bad weather on maritime operations is much greater today than in the past. Until the wars of the French Revolution it was common for the fleets to stay in harbour during the winter months, a practice finally stopped by Lord St Vincent when enforcing a continuous blockade of French ports throughout the year. Even so, the weather did not have a dominating effect on naval operations since its effects were the same on both fleets. If the battleships of one fleet, sail or steam, were slowed down or otherwise affected by the weather the Admiral could be confident that his opponent was experiencing similar problems.

Modern maritime operations involve submarines and aircraft as well as surface ships and, though all these vehicles are affected by the weather, they are affected in different ways and at different times. The effectiveness of one category may be seriously impaired while its enemy retains 100% capability. This article will look at how weather is measured and how often it occurs in different parts of the ocean. A later article will expand on the effect of weather in the surface ship and how the naval architect designs a ship to minimise such effects.

The earliest system of measurement was introduced in the 1830s by Rear-Admiral Sir Francis Beaufort, the Hydrographer. He related the strength of the wind to the amount of sail that could be carried and, with some changes, his scale is still in use. It is important to note that the Beaufort Number relates only to wind speed and does not directly say anything about wave height. Note that the current definition in terms of wind speed is slightly different from the original.

Wind blowing over the surface of the sea will generate waves but it takes some considerable time and distance before the wave heights reach their maximum. The stronger the wind, the greater the fetch needed before the highest waves appear. For example, in a Force 7, at least 108 miles are needed for waves to be fully developed. In consequence, the earlier European naval wars, with fighting in the North Sea, English Channel and Mediterranean, were rarely exposed to fully developed seas. The shallow waters in many of these areas does, however, lead to very steep waves.

Since World War II, wave height has been described in terms of sea state, a number which relates to the observed height. The wave height is taken as the average of the one third highest waves in a confused sea. Comparison between observation and measurement shows that this definition – significant wave height – agrees quite well with the subjective view of an experienced observer. Use of a scale related to wave height alone is inadequate since it gives no timescale. Length of wave, closely related to the square of the period, is important as a small boat, for instance would not feel bad in a 2 metre sea and a period of 15 seconds but the same height with a period of 5 seconds would seem very nasty.

Table 2 shows sea state, significant wave height, the number of days a year on which these wave heights are likely in the North Atlantic and the wind speed (Beaufort Number) that would produce these waves in the open ocean.

Wind and sea states vary considerably from one part of the ocean to another. Table 3 shows the percentage occurrence of various sea states over the whole of the Atlantic and for the whole North Sea area both over the year and in winter. In addition, data is included from two weather ships, *India*, well off Northern Scotland (19°W 59°N) and *Famita* off Norway (3°E 57°30'N).

What does all this mean in ability to fight? As the sea gets rough, men get tired and sometimes sea sick, their capability to make a correct judgement diminishes and even simple physical tasks take much longer. It becomes increasingly difficult to land and handle a helicopter, the efficiency of weapons and sensors (particularly sonars) is degraded. Details are closely guarded secrets but the following broad indications have been released.

Helicopter operations the limiting conditions are: average roll less than 5°, vertical velocity of deck due to pitch and heave less than 2 metres a second and half that for transverse velocity.

In general for a 110m (361ft) frigate up to Sea State 4 there is little or no effect on fighting efficiency. At Sea State 5 (31% of the year) the ship will be rolling 3° either way, if stabilised, pitching 1½° and heave through 1 metre. Speed is reduced to about 24 knots. Every job takes longer, the motion is seen as inconvenient and some sensors are affected. Replenishment is possible but difficult.

In Sea State 6 (21% of the year) the ship is rolling 4°, pitching 2° and heaving 1.5 metres. Speed will be 20 knots. Up to a third of the crew will be sick and all are

TABLE 1: FROM FINCHAM MASTING 1840

Beaufort Number	Description	Pressure (lb/in²)	Wind Speed (knots)	Sails		Today Revised Wind Speed (knots)
11-12	Hurricane		60-100			over 56
	Storm		45-50			
10	Heavy Gale	7.35/9	40	Close reef main topsls, storm stay sail or closed reefed main topsl only		48-55
9	Strong Gale	5/7	34	Reefed courses, close reef main topsl Take in main in rough seas		41-47
8	Fresh Gale	4/5	28	Close reefed topsls. Reefed courses Take in spanker and jib		34-40
7	Moderate Gale	2.5/3.5	23	2-3 reef topsl		28-33
6	Strong Breeze	1.5/2.3	15-20	Single reef topsl and topgallants In heavy seas 2 reef & take in topgallant		22-27
5	Fresh Breeze	.6/1.3	14	Royals & flying jib in. In heavy seas 2 reef topsail	Plain sail. Jibs, fore & main course driver, 3 topsails 3 topgallants	17-21
4	Moderate Breeze	.4/.45	13	All sail		11-16
3	Gentle Breeze	.2/.3	8	All sail		7-10
2	Light Breeze	.1/.14	5	All sail		4-6
1	Light Airs	0-0.05		All sail		1-3

TABLE 2: NORTH ATLANTIC SEA STATES

Sea State	Wave Height (metres)	No of days per year N Atlantic	Fully developed sea		Notes
			Beaufort	Wind Speed (knots)	
0-2	0-0.5		0-3	0-10	Calm
3	0.5-1.25	55	4	11-16	Large wavelets. Crests beginning to break
4	1.25-2.5	153	5	17-21	Small waves becoming larger, numerous whitecaps
5	2.5-4	99	6	22-27	Moderate waves. Many whitecaps, some spray
6	4-6	40	7-9	28-47	Larger waves forming whitecaps everywhere. More spray
7 & over	over 6	18	10 & over	over 48	Sea heaps up, white foam blown in streaks

TABLE 3: SEA STATE AS A PERCENTAGE OF THE YEAR

Sea State	N Atlantic			India		North Sea		Famita (winter)
	All Year	Winter	All Year	Winter	All Year	Winter		
0-3	15	9	8	2	36	27	11	
4	42	34	31	3	44	43	33	
5	27	32	31	27	15	20	33	
6	11	17	21	48	5	8	15	
7 & over	5	8	9	20	2	2	5	

fatigued. Sleep is difficult as is helicopter operation. Many weapon systems are degraded.

Sea State 7 (9% of the year) the ship is ineffective as a fighting unit. She will roll about 10°, pitch 2½° or more and heave at least 2 metres. At best, the speed will be reduced to 10 knots.

Particularly in Northern waters the loss of efficiency is serious. The notes above show slight loss of efficiency 31% of the year, appreciable loss over 21%, and total ineffectiveness for 9%. A later article will show how the naval architect designs new ships to minimise the effects of bad weather.

US ASW SSK Submarines

by Norman Friedman

It is so common, now, to read that submarines are the only effective counters to other submarines that one might reasonably wonder why that was not so during the last great ASW war, 1939-1945, or just how this truth came to be understood. In its time, the concept of submarines as ASW platforms was quite radical, and submarine services, such as that of the United States, adopted it only relatively slowly and with considerable reluctance. The catalyst was the 1944 shock of the German Type XXI U-boat, which the Western navies expected the Soviets to duplicate rapidly and in great numbers after 1945. So poorly did existing ASW systems perform against the Type XXI that both major Western navies were quite willing to adopt radical expedients. The ASW submarine or, in American terms, the SSK, was one of several.

The problem was that a very fast submarine could evade existing surface ship sonars almost at will. Operating at high frequency, the latter were limited to ranges between 1500 and 3000 yards and there was little hope that enough sonar-equipped escorts could be provided to ring a convoy with solid coverage. As in World War II, then, much would have to depend on catching submarines once they revealed themselves by attacking. However, a Type XXI was so fast that, submerged, it could often outrun existing escorts. Hence the pressure to build fast escorts postwar, or to convert destroyers as an interim solution: the existing slow frigates and corvettes just could not expect to cope.

PRECEDENTS FROM 1914-18 AND 1939-45

Given the probable failure of convoy tactics, the best solution was somehow to deal with the submarine before it could reach its patrol area. Possible solutions included mining Soviet waters, and attacking Soviet submarine bases. The other possibility was to intercept transiting submarines. This was not a new idea. During World War I, faced with the apparent failure of most ASW measures, the Admiralty assigned British submarines to patrol both German transit routes and U-boat patrol areas, reasoning that submerged submarines could ambush surfaced U-boats. This idea was rational because, to make good any considerable distance, a submarine had to proceed on the surface. British submarines did again patrol German waters during World War II, but a much greater proportion of U-boats were sunk by convoy escorts and by aircraft, the latter often directed on the basis of long-range locators such as HF/DF, and actually locating surfaced submarines by means of radar.

Aircraft were, at least theoretically, far more efficient than surface ships or submarines because they were much faster, and therefore could be employed in more limited numbers. But they were ineffective against submerged submarines because they had no long-range detector that could penetrate the surface of the water. Thus the advent of the Type XXI, which would almost always operate submerged, was a disaster for the Allies: their most effective ASW systems were negated.

BARRIER STRATEGIES

The only compensation was that, in order to reach its operating area, a submarine had to snorkel, and snorkelling was quite noisy. Although existing surface ship sonars were not well suited to passive operation, it was soon discovered that suitably silenced submarines could detect snorkellers at appreciable ranges. Hence the concept of the SSK: a submarine equipped with a large passive sonar and homing torpedoes, and placed athwart the probable transit route of enemy submarines. The number of SSKs depended upon the effective engagement range: the longer the range of sensor and torpedoes, the fewer might be needed to maintain a barrier of a given length. As first formulated, the SSK strategy was to station submarines very close to Soviet bases, so that relatively few submarines would be able to slip by. However, more modern concepts entail the use of relatively long-range systems, and that in turn permits a small number of more expensive SSKs to patrol a much longer barrier line. Hence the current NATO concept of the Greenland-Iceland-United Kingdom Gap (GIUK) barrier, to protect vital shipping in the North Atlantic.

In practice, there was no expectation that a submarine barrier would be leak-proof. However, even a relatively leaky barrier could whittle down the Soviet submarine force quite rapidly, because each submarine would have to pass through the barrier both at the beginning and at the end of each patrol. For example, imagine a barrier capable of killing only 20 per cent of the submarines trying to penetrate it. That would amount to a net probability of 36 per cent that any submarine would be sunk either before or after its patrol, not counting other ASW measures. The average submarine would survive only two such patrols.

From 1947 onwards, US scientists experimented with carefully-silenced submarines listening at very low frequencies; they discovered the convergence zone effect, by means of which sounds can be detected at extreme ranges (in typical conditions, at multiples of about 35 miles). At the same time, the US Navy, which before and during World War II had concentrated on high-frequency acoustics, began to experiment with the low-frequency equipment developed by the German Navy. One system in particular excited interest: GHG, an array of passive sonars. It became the US BQR-4, the basis of the SSK programme.

US 1948 ASW PLANS

The FY48 Program included a specialised anti-submarine submarine (SSK), which would lie in wait on enemy transit routes, listening for snorkellers and for surface transits. The new technology of acoustic torpedoes would provide the weapon. At this time it was assumed that a submarine would have to snorkel virtually continuously to make good any considerable distance as it transitted towards its patrol area. It was clear from the first that very large numbers of such ASW submarines would be needed. In 1948 American ASW planners expected a short-term Soviet fleet of 356 modern submarines, and a long-term threat of 2000.

USS K1, lead boat of the SSK class, on 8 November 1951 two days before her official completion by Electric Boat. She had been laid down on 1 July 1949 and launched on 2 March 1951. Her most important feature is the massive BQR-4 passive sonar dome in the bows. She was renamed *Barracuda* in December 1955 and withdrawn from the SSK role in 1959 to become training boat *T1* until reclassification as an attack boat on 1 August 1972. She was stricken in 1973 long after her two younger sisters.
US Navy

On these bases they were able to calculate production requirements for the special submarines; three boats were needed to keep one on station in the forward areas. They would operate near Soviet bases, and also in barrier formations in the open sea. Others, whose numbers were not calculated, might form barriers around convoy routes, or work with hunter-killer teams. Two different strategies are evident. Against the immediate 356-submarine threat, the ASW submarines would operate well inshore, near the Soviet bases:

	On station	Total
North Cape-Cherry Island-Spitzbergen	56	168
Petropavlovsk (Soviet Far East base)	6	18
North End Sakhalin (Sea of Okhotsk)	6	18
La Perouse Strait (Japan/Sakhalin)	7	21
Tsugaru Strait (Hokkaido/Honshu, Japan)	2	6
Training		19
Total	77	250

Against the longer-term threat, however, they would form barriers much farther out to sea. The reasoning of the time is not clear, but there may have been an assumption that Soviet ASW would be much more effective by the time the 2000-boat fleet materialised, perhaps about 1960. Presumably the numbers were all predicated on

an assumed 20,000-yard range against a snorkeller:

Greenland-Iceland-		
Scotland	124	372
NE Pacific Coast		
Kamchatka Peninsula	10	30
Wales-Spain	86	258
Petropavlovsk	6	18
Kuriles	30	90
Tsugaru	2	6
Kyushu-China	42	126
Training		70
Total	210	970

Note the need to seal the southern exit of the English Channel in the 2000-submarine case. Presumably it was expected that minefields in the Baltic would seal in the Baltic Fleet in either case. By this time a snorkelling submarine had been detected out to first convergence zone, 35 miles, and there were claims that 'any submarine which exceeds cavitation speed becomes noisy and would be detected. They give up quiet operations when they exceed 6 knots . . .'

Modern sonars are much more effective. Although the breakdown of US submarine functions by number is classified, clearly the number required to fill the GIUK Gap barrier cannot much exceed ten. There are only about 90 attack submarines altogether, some of which are rated as 'second line' and thus probably excluded from so demanding an assignment. Each carrier battle group is to have one or two, which suggests a total of about ten submarines so occupied in peacetime at any one time (or 30 so dedicated, given the usual ratio); others would surely be assigned to convoys, to the Pacific, even to SSBN escort duty. In that case the ratio of early ASW submarines to current-type attack submarines is probably about ten to one, for the same barrier. That is probably not far from the ratio of sonar ranges, which suggests that current types expect to detect targets at about two or three convergence zones (say up to 210,000 yards or 100 miles), although attacks will occur at much shorter ranges. Another way to look at these figures is to suggest that any very severe reduction in US passive sonar range would effectively destroy the barrier strategy, since impossible numbers would be required.

SSK DESIGN

In 1948 the proposed solution was a boat so simple that it could be mass produced, even by builders not familiar with submarine practice in wartime. It was not a fast submarine, but it is included here because it was directly inspired by the advent of the Type XXI. The major simplification was to trade submarine performance (hence size) for *torpedo* performance. Much slower than attack submarines, at 8.5 knots submerged (one-hour rate; 6 knots when snorkelling), the very quiet SSK would not have to close its targets. Instead, it would

detect them passively at 20,000 yards or more, and attack with fast homing torpedoes.

The design was adapted to mass production and operation in several ways. First, it was limited to a diving depth of 400ft, where the new attack submarines were intended for 700ft. Given its low submerged speed, there was no need to be able to rig in the bow planes. The carefully silenced diesel engine was 'packaged' for unit replacement at a forward base, and the engine room was to be unmanned, to reduce crew size. A contemporary Navy account suggests that silencing was expected to be

USS *K3* off Mare Island (N of San Francisco) on her completion day by that yard (11 February 1952). She was laid down on 17 March 1950 and launched on 21 June 1951. Above her BQR-4 bow sonar is the BQS-3 'single ping' active sonar installation. She was renamed *Bonita* in December 1955 and ceased her SSK role in 1959 after 1958 service as a nuclear test target (superficial damage), serving as attack boat SS 552 until stricken in April 1965 along with *Bass* (ex-*K2*).
US Navy

easier for a small, low-powered diesel; the original design showed a single screw.

The SSK did follow attack submarine design standards in having no conning tower in its sail; instead a command and information centre was combined with the control room. It also resembled the larger submarines in having a passive sonar in a chin position. Mission requirements included provision for underwater anchoring on a picket station and paired fathometers, one on the keel and one atop the hull, tiltable for under-ice operation.

As in many other warship design projects, size kept creeping upward. In the case of the SSK, the original 480-ton hull could not fit enough batteries to allow for sufficient loiter time. It turned out that even passive electronic equipment was a sufficient drain on battery charge to require much more capacity. And by the time the SSK was ordered it had grown to 750 tons, with two propellers in place of the original one, and four rather than two torpedo tubes. It was also limited to production by specialised yards. In the event just three were completed between November 1951 and February 1952.

The huge BQR-4 passive sonar, 20 × 10 × 10ft, was expected to have sufficient bearing descrimination to permit the submarine to close a target. Design sketches show it wrapped around the SSK sail, but it was actually installed in the bow, presumably for better isolation from engine and propeller noise. This installation was typical of later American ASW submarine practice. The higher-frequency BQR-2 (the sole sonar of the original design, adapted from the German *Balkon*), was a 3ft high circular array of vertical line hydrophones, 5ft in diameter, in a keel dome. With a claimed bearing accuracy of 1/10 of a degree, it would be used for fire control (attack). A hydrophone could be suspended clear of the hull for very long range (but non-directional) listening, and there was also a modified World War II JT passive sonar (BQR-3) intended as a back-up for the newer sets. Although space and weight were reserved for the possible installation of an active sonar, none was ever fitted.

Performance was spectacular: off Bermuda in 1952, the prototype, *K1*, detected a snorkeller at 30 miles, and tracked it for five hours. Even so, no mass production was ordered. Even though it was too large for true mass

production, in service the SS proved too small to withstand the rough conditions of its projected wartime operating area.

The only other source of large numbers of submarines was the numerous survivors of the war-built attack submarine fleet. An SSK conversion programme was one of several parallel ASW initiatives: the others were the projected mass conversion of *Fletcher* class destroyers (to DDE, 18 were completed before the programme was dropped) and the ASW conversion of existing light carriers (CVL). In each case, new construction was considered preferable, but it was inconceivable, given the sheer size of the newly-completed wartime fleet. In the case of the SSK, the conversion programme was conceived as a parallel source of submarines rather than as a replacement, since the problems of the original design were not evident until well after the conversions were underway. Although only seven boats were actually converted (the prototype, *Grouper*, in the FY50 Program, and six others under the FY52 Program, all before the original SSK had been completed), the design of the contemporary attack submarine conversion (the 'Guppy') was arranged to facilitate later SSK conversion. Moreover, other submarines were converted to a 'fleet snorkel' configuration which itself was designed for relatively easy conversion to 'Guppy' status.

The first of the conversions, *Grouper* (SSK 214), had her BQR-4 array wrapped around the front of her sail, but later boats had their BQR-4s in their bows, displacing two of the six forward torpedo tubes. Although ultra-quiet operation had originally been needed, the Bureau of Ships was able to modify these submarines to the point where they could listen while running equipment such as air conditioners, which, according to an official account of the period, 'improved habitability and also reduced electronic maintenance problems'.

SSK EXERCISES
By the mid-1950s, then, the SSK concept was well understood and well accepted. It had, moreover, been proven operationally. A February 1954 exercise SW of Iceland illustrates SSK tactics and performance. The new *K1* operated against the converted fleet submarine *Cavalla*, for a total of 36 runs. *K1* achieved an average detection range of 28 miles (11 runs); *Cavalla* was limited to an average of 13 miles (25 runs). In 26 cases one submarine or the other was able to get into attack position, and 21 attacks were judged successful. By this time the big BQR-4 was being used for attack as well as search and track; it was credited with half-degree accuracy at firing range. *K1* used the new technique of estimating range by plotting target motion as she manoeuvred, but she was limited by errors due to an insufficiently stable gyro; she could not adequately measure her own motion.

One run began at a range of 60 miles, the target submarine *Cavella* running for 2 hours on batteries at noncavitating speed (4.5 knots), alternating with 1 hour snorkelling at 6 knots, while zigzagging (short legs superimposed on longer ones to make target motion analysis difficult). She was essentially undetectable while on batteries. Even so, contact was made at 38 miles, and 6 hours and 35 minutes later the ambushing *K1* was in attack position, 1200 yards off the target's beam. This remarkable performance was attributed to the effectiveness of the self-noise reduction programme and to the range of the BQR-4 array sonar, about ten times that of the wartime JT. By 1955 it was being credited with 10-50 miles.

The great defect of the SSK was its limited speed: it could detect a target much farther away than it could attack. Several solutions were tried. The SSK could relay data to a destroyer by underwater telephone, which had a range of 8-11 miles but also disclosed the submarine's position. Alternatively it could vector in a carrier- or land-based attack airplane. Patrol plane-SSK operations were quite common in the 1950s; reportedly the Atlantic Fleet war plan included an SSK-air barrier off Argentia (Newfoundland) barring Soviet submarines from the US East Coast, as late as 1962. This concept survives in some forms of 'direct support' of battle groups. Finally, the submarine itself could be provided with a much longer-range weapon, which became Subroc, the underwater-launched ballistic ASW missile, with a nuclear depth bomb warhead. Subroc was generally employed in combination with a more effective sonar, the spherical BQQ-2, in nuclear submarines, but it was conceived in the SSK era.

THE NUCLEAR SSK
By 1955 it was clear that the next stage was a nuclear SSK with a new and more powerful sonar. By this time the nuclear reactor designers had obtained sufficient experience to propose a range of powerplants, including a small one, of about 2500shp, which might be used to power a very small submarine. In January 1955, for example, a Bureau of Ships study of future warship designs included a 900-ton SSKN powered by a 1500shp engine, its bow filled with sonars, and the torpedo tubes abaft it, angled outwards. This must have been the origin of the USS *Tullibee*.

There were two problems. First, SSKs had to be small and cheap. Nuclear endurance on station could reduce the numerical requirements drastically, particularly if the barrier could achieve its results very early in a war, before the boats had to be relieved on station. Although all nuclear powerplants were expensive, clearly a small SSKN would be more economical than a large one. The other problem was more difficult: noise. The first nuclear submarines were extremely noisy. Partly this was due to the use of geared turbines with their inherent whine. Partly, too, however, it was a consequence of the nature of the nuclear reactor itself, which required constant pumping of coolant. In the SSKN design, gearing noise was eliminated by shifting to turbo-electric propulsion, which, if inherently quieter, was also a larger consumer of internal space. The pump problem may have been more tractable at lower power levels.

Unfortunately, just as in the case of the original SSK, the SSKN grew uncontrollably, to displace about 2300 tons (with 2500shp). It did introduce the new sonar replacement for BQR-4, the BQQ-1 (later BQQ-2) that

USS *K3* in April 1954 when she and *K2* were based at Pearl Harbor. The class displaced 765 tons standard (1160 tons submerged), measured 196ft 1in oa × 24ft 7in × 14ft 5in and carried a crew of 37 with 4 × 21in torpedo tubes (2 bow and 2 stern). Twin GM diesels gave a surface speed of 13 knots and 8.5 knots submerged (1050shp).

US Navy

included a massive spherical transducer occupying the bow. It was the submarine equivalent of the surface ships' SQS-26, and ranges as great as 50 miles were claimed for it. Although the nuclear submarine *Thresher* of 1960 was not fitted to fire it, her sonar was later linked with a new type of underwater weapon, the Subroc ballistic missile, fired from underwater at a submarine target. In theory, Subroc was the ideal SSK barrier weapon, since it could engage targets at the ranges the new sonar made possible. In practice, Subroc is less than ideal because it is a nuclear weapon, subject to the very strong political and policy constraints of such systems. Its successor, SOW, will probably be a non-nuclear version, armed with the new Mark 50 Advanced Light Weight Torpedo (Barracuda).

For FY58 the issue was whether or not to build a new SSKN based on *Tullibee*. For some years the US Navy had been pursuing two parallel courses, the specialist SSK and the general-purpose attack submarine.

Although the latter could carry ASW torpedoes, it was much more a lineal descendant of past attack submarines, which were primarily means of dealing with surface ships. This orientation appears not to have been questioned, even though the Soviet surface fleet of the day was a minor problem compared to the threat of Soviet submarines.

The key decision was that, in future, there would be only one type of submarine, aside from such clearly specialist types as missile and radar picket craft. *All* submarines would have SSK capability; similarly, all would be capable of attacking surface ships. In practice, with the anti-ship role no longer opposed to the ASW role, ASW came to predominate, to such an extent that it is now the principal role, and indeed the justification, of the nuclear attack submarine force. However, current nuclear attack submarines are so much more mobile than their SSK ancestors that the barrier may not be the best way to use them; in that sense the SSK concept may be on its way out.

From a physical point of view, this particular compromise was reflected in the two major design features of the new *Thresher* (now, with the loss of the prototype, *Permit*) class. One was high (but now silenced) power, the attribute of the attack submarine. Turbo-electric

USS Bream (SS 243), off Oahu 29 January 1962, was a more conventional fleet boat/SSK with an enlarged bow housing the BQR-4 passive sonar. The small dome above it carried a BQS-3 active set. Another active sonar is in the smaller dome farther aft.
US Navy

USS *Grouper* (SSK 214) of Mare Island Naval Shipyard in June 1951. She was the first of seven fleet submarines to be converted to the SSK role. Her BQR-4 sonar was wrapped around the front of the bridge fairweather. Although at first glance she appears to be a conventional 'Guppy', the men on her bridge are some distance away from its front edge and, unlike a 'Guppy', it has no upper level windows.
US Navy

drive was considered, but it was rejected because of the design delay entailed. Instead, the geared drive of the most recent attack class was retained, but the engines and gearing were mounted on a raft, sound-isolated from the hull of the submarine. This made for a materially larger submarine. The other major feature was the big bow sonar of *Tullibee*, combined, as in that boat, with torpedo tubes located abaft the bow, and angled outward. These two features, high (but relatively quiet) speed and a big bow sonar, have characterised both subsequent US attack submarine designs, the *Sturgeon* (launched 1963-71) and the *Permit* (launched 1961-66). In that sense the SSK idea had triumphed.

During the 1960s, Admiral Hyman G Rickover tried to revive the distinction between the fast attack submarine and the slower, but much quieter, barrier submarine, proposing that the United States build two parallel nuclear classes: the *Los Angeles* for attack and some development of the *Glenard P Lipscomb* or *Narwhal* for the barrier mission. Economics made this impossible. However, this time the decision went against the specialist barrier submarine, because the faster *Los Angeles*, which was almost as quiet, could carry out a new type of ASW mission, the direct support of fast carrier groups. At the same time she was quiet enough for barrier work.

From time to time the submarine, with its superior sonar performance, was proposed as the primary anti-submarine vehicle. For example, in February 1962, Rear Admiral Ralph K James, who was then Chief of the Bureau of Ships, suggested that in future surface ASW ships should be confined to use in shallow water and in protecting convoys that might also be threatened by air attack.

NOTE
Much of this article has been adapted from Norman Friedman's forthcoming book *Submarine Design and Development* to be published in May 1984 by Conway Maritime Press at £15.

Was there a Serbian Navy?

by René Greger

Maybe readers will smile when reading this title as none of them will have ever met any mention of a Serbian Navy in the naval literature issued before or during World War I. But they would smile too soon. It is fact that there was neither a Serbian regular navy or river flotilla but there were ships flying the Serbian ensign (red, blue and white stripes with the Serbian eagle in the middle) both on the Danube and in the Adriatic and Aegean Seas during 1914-18.

When World War I broke out in July 1914 Serbia did not have any seacoast, but the frontier between old rivals, the Austro-Hungarian Empire and the young and small Serbian kingdom, was formed by three great rivers; the Drina in the west, the Danube and the Sava in the north.

Austria-Hungary had a very strong river flotilla including numerous auxiliaries. Its monitors armed with 120mm (4.7in) guns could influence operations on the whole front excluding the wild Drina. On the other hand very poor Serbia could not afford to spend money building river warships of a similar type, quite apart from the fact that she lacked the trained sailors to man them. The first river transport organisation in Serbia (*Srpsko Brodarsko Drustvo*) was only established in 1890. At that time there was just one river vessel in the country – the passenger steamer *Deligrad* owned by the government from 1862. Serbia therefore asked her allies for help and received it.

At the end of August 1914 a group of 106 Russian seamen appeared on the Sava river and installed there the first torpedo battery and laid 12 mines. British and French groups followed soon, bringing torpedoes and naval guns. While the Russians concentrated on minelaying and had great success with it sinking the Austrian monitor *Temes*, the British expedition led by Vice-Admiral Troubridge tried to use torpedoes against the aggressive monitors. The torpedo batteries installed on the land had no success but a British picket boat caused the Austrians some trouble. This large steam boat under the command of Lieutenant-Commander Kerr was armed with torpedo launching apparatus (if not tubes?) and attacked the Austrian monitors anchored at Zemun on the evening of 22 April 1915. Two years later, the British Prize Court made a declaration that the commander, officers and crew were entitled to prize money amounting to £514 for the destruction of the Austrian monitor *Koros* in the Danube. In fact the Austrian vessel was not hit and the following attack on 17 May against an Austrian patrol boat also failed. Both attacks made by the British boat, operating (according to some unconfirmed sources) under the Serbian flag,

were the only river operations undertaken from the Serbian side.

The Russian 'Special Expedition' sent no combat boats to the front, but tried to protect the convoys of supply ships sent from Russia to Serbia up the Danube. The most important stretch – the Iron Gates – was to be defended by the armed Russian steamer *Tiraspol* and two motor gunboats originally used on the Amur, against possible raids. This never happened. Not known is the existence of a Serbian ship, manned by the Army, which took part in the defence of Russian convoys coming to the small Serbian port of Prahovo. Armed with a machine gun, the tug *Stig* was to protect the supply ships against Austrian aircraft. When Bulgaria attacked Serbia in October 1915 all ships on the Serbian bank had to be scuttled or tried to reach the Rumanian port of Corabia. *Stig* was scuttled.

The tug *Stig* manned by the Serbian Army on the Danube in 1915.
Author's collection

The torpedo boat *Srbija* in the Gulf of Salonika 1916-18.
Author's collection

Several weeks later the defeated Serbian Army reached the Adriatic coast of Albania after a long and distressful retreat. About 140,000 remaining Serbian soldiers were evacuated by Allied ships from Durazzo and Valona to Corfu by the end of March 1916. On that Greek island the tired Serbs were placed in many camps and communication between them was difficult. At first some Greek private boats were hired, but the Army Command and Serbian Government wanted a vessel of their own. Besides this the Prince Regent (later King Alexander I) had had a bad experience, not having any boat or vessel under his own command, during the final phase of the Serbian retreat in Albania at the end of January. On the morning of 21 January he came from evacuated Scutari to the small port of Medua and wished to be transported as soon as possible to Valona. There were two small Italian destroyers in the harbour, waiting for the old Montenegrian King Nicholas I who left his defeated small kingdom with his whole court. Personal relations between Alexander and his old uncle Nicholas were far from good, especially after the bombing attempt organised against Nicholas by Alexander's family. Alexander had to wait until Nicholas' entourage came and, after a brief public conversation with his uncle, he was informed by the Italian commander that he

The torpedo boat *Srbija* at Salonika in 1918. Her crew are in French Navy uniform and her funnel bands represent Serbia's national colours in the red, blue and white ensign at the stern.
Author's collection

would be transported to Valona via Brindisi after Nicholas and his court had left the ships in that Italian harbour. The enraged Alexander refused that proposal, mounted a horse and left Medua with his retinue for Durazzo by land, Alexander never forgot this incident and wished to have a vessel under the Serbian flag.

Fortunately an old Greek former torpedo boat, named *Paxo* (or *Paxoi*?) was discovered in the main harbour of Corfu and bought for 50,000 drachmas (about £2000 at that time). The vessel received the name *Srbija* (according to another serious source the name was *Velika Srbija* ie The Great Serbia). Not many of her technical details could be found in later Yugoslav documents except the length 23.1m (75ft 9in), beam 4m (13ft 1in) and a speed of 16 knots. She was probably one of four French-built small torpedo boats, bought in 1880 for the Greek Navy and deleted from the list in 1910. According to standard naval yearbooks they had the length of 22m (72ft 2in) and beam of 3.96m (13ft). Their crew was 12 men the same number as the Serbs who could be met in the ship in 1918.

The rested and reorganised Serbian Army was transported to the Salonika Front in May 1916 and the small *Srbija* had to follow. Her inexperienced crew did not dare risk the passage on their own and so the vessel was towed by a French destroyer to Patras. Perhaps a diplomatic incident between Italy and Serbia also influenced this solution. Italy protested against the use of the 'unknown and internationally not allowed' Serbian flag at sea. Only after the Serbian Government promised that the vessel would not be armed, did Italy cease to protest. Italy's fear that Yugoslav warships would appear in *mare nostrum* (ie the Adriatic) was just as acute as between the wars.

Srbija served under the Serbian flag in the Gulf of Salonika up to November 1918 and later as one of the first vessels under the new Yugoslav flag in Boka Kotorska during the early 1920s. She was never armed in spite of her official Yugoslav classification as '*torpiljer*' (torpedo boat) and she was scrapped in 1928.

THE LAST SUPER DESTROYERS?
Mogador & Kléber Classes

by Robert Dumas

The *Mogador* class destroyers were the ultimate evolution of their type in France. By virtue of their dimensions and their armament these two ships were the biggest conventional destroyers ever built; indeed they could have been classified as light cruisers like the Italian 'Capitani Romani' class (see *Warship* 7 and 8). They were an enlargement of the *Fantasque* class, the French designers aiming to increase their offensive power by

installing twin-pseudo turrets (fully enclosed gunhouses) with 5.5in (138.6mm) guns.

Mogador was built under the 1932 budget and *Volta* under that of 1934.

BUILDING
Mogador, named after the Moroccan seaport, was built at Lorient Dockyard, *Volta*, named after the West African river, by Ateliers et Chantiers de Bretagne at Nantes.

	Laid down	Launched	In service
Mogador	28.12.34	9.6.37	10.8.38
Volta	24.12.34	20.8.37	21.3.39

Mogador at Le Havre, 12 November 1938, three months after her completion. A twin 13.2mm Model 1929 machine gun mounting can be seen below the bridge.

Author's collection

Mogador at the same juncture. Super destroyers obviously had no new means of drying laundry!
Author's collection

Their main armament was not ready when they entered service and their proving trials continued afterwards.

CHARACTERISTICS

Displacement	2884 tons standard, 3500-3600 tons normal, 4018 tons full load
Length overall	137.5m/451ft 2in
Length between perpendiculars	131m/429ft 9in
Beam (maximum)	12.67m/41ft 7in
Beam (waterline)	12.56m/41ft 2in
Draught	3.65-4.57m/12-15ft
Main armament	8 × 5.5in/45 Model 1934 guns in 4 twin mounts (30° elevation)
Anti-aircraft armament	2 × 37mm CAD Model 1933 guns 4 × 13.2mm Model 1929 Hotchkiss machine guns in twin mounts

Note: I have found that 8mm Hotchkiss Model 1916 machine guns were mounted in *Volta*, a twin mount and one single on the after deckhouse (on the centreline of the ship) and two singles in the bridge wings. It was intended eventually to carry 40 mines (Breguet 500kg/1100lb type).

Ammunition	1440 rounds of 5.5in plus 85 starshell 2480 rounds of 37mm
Torpedo tubes	10 × 550mm/21.7in in two triple and two twin mounts
Rangefinders	2 × 5m/16ft 5in (one for the main director, one for the foretop) 1 × 4m/13ft 1in Type A for the after director 2 × 1m/39in for the anti-aircraft guns (one for the forward 13.2mm machine gun platform and one abaft the after director)
Searchlights	2 × 75cm (port and starboard of the after funnel) 2 × 45cm/17.7in (port and starboard of the main director)

Mogador from astern at the same time. Her name has yet to be painted on in the regular fashion on the quarter not far from the stern depth charge chutes (24 440lb DCs was the normal large destroyer armament).

Author's collection

Boats	2 × 7m/23ft motor launches (port and starboard of the forward funnel)
	2 × 7m/23ft motor pinnacles (abaft the forward funnel)
	1 × 5m/16ft dinghy between the pinnaces
	1 × 3m/9ft pram stowed in the dinghy
	1 × 7m/23ft whaler on derricks to starboard
	1 × 7m/23ft rowing cutter on derricks to port
Machinery	4 Indret vertical small-tube boilers with superheating
	4 collectors and 2 superheaters of air
	Boiler pressure 35kg/sq cm
	Superheater temperature 385° C
	2-shaft Rateau-Bretagne geared steam turbines of 92,000shp and 105,000shp
Speed	39 knots
Trials	*Mogador* over 8 hours: at 3512 tons, 104,925shp = 41.274 knots in 9th hour: at 3098 tons, 118,320shp = 43.45 knots
	Volta over 8 hours: at 3168 tons,? = 42.09 knots in 9th hour: at 3105 tons,? = 43.78 knots
Oil	310 tons normal load, 710 tons maximum
Range	4000 miles at 18 knots
	3000 miles at 20 knots
Crew	251 peacetime (15 officers, 41 petty officers, 195 ratings)
	264 wartime (15 officres, 249 ratings)
	284 flagship

MODIFICATIONS

Both ships had a cap fitted to the forward funnel, probably at the end of 1938. A steel bulwark was built round the 13.2mm machine gun platform (early 1940).

In *Mogador* the searchlight was plated (spring 1940). During the major repairs following the damage she sustained at Mers el Kebir it was decided to alter her armament. Number 3 turret was removed and Number 4 was raised. The anti-aircraft armament was increased by six 37mm Model 1933 guns in twin mounts on the after deckhouse. It is likely that *Volta*'s armament would also have been augmented. (The photographs of the scuttled

1

2

3

1 *Mogador* moored at Brest in December 1939 after one of the Allied searches for *Scharnhorst* and *Gneisenau*. She was repainted in the superstructure light grey early in the New Year.
ECPA/Author's collection

2 *Volta* steams off Toulon early in 1941 after her AA armament had been increased. The battlecruiser *Strasbourg* can just be seen above her stern.
Author's collection

3 *Mogador* at the end of 1940 showing her amputated stern caused by a direct hit from a British 15in shell at Mers et Kebir 3 July 1940. She had begun to sink by the stern on fire but the main engine bulkheads stood firm enabling her to be towed and beached out of harm's way. She still contributed AA fire on 6 July when *Dunkerque* was cripped by *Ark Royal's* Swordfish.
Author's collection

Mogador do not show any guns still on the after deckhouse.) The number of oil fuel bunkers was increased.

In *Volta* the foretop rangefinder was given a steel roof (end 1940). Two 13.2mm CAS Browning machine guns were installed on small platforms on either side of Number 3 turret (early 1941). At the end of 1941 or beginning of 1942 the Hotchkiss machine guns were removed from the platform forward of the bridge. They were replaced by two 25mm Hotchkiss guns. Finally two 13.2mm CAS Browning guns were installed on new platforms to port and starboard of the navigation bridge. The 37mm gun shields were strengthened as was the Type A rangefinder tower. The searchlight tower was closed in as in *Mogador*. Finally extra ammunition lockers were fitted for the 37mm mounting on the forward platform and lifejacket holders fixed to stanchions on the navigation bridge.

COLOUR SCHEME AND MARKINGS
Both ships had dark grey hulls from the end of 1939 to the beginning of 1940 with a light grey superstructure. The latter colour was extended to the whole of both ships for the rest of their existence.

Until 21 March 1939 *Mogador* and *Volta* carried the hull numbers 4 and 5 respectively. From that date they were changed to X61 and X62 in white, becoming brick red from April 1940. Both ships carried a blue band on

108

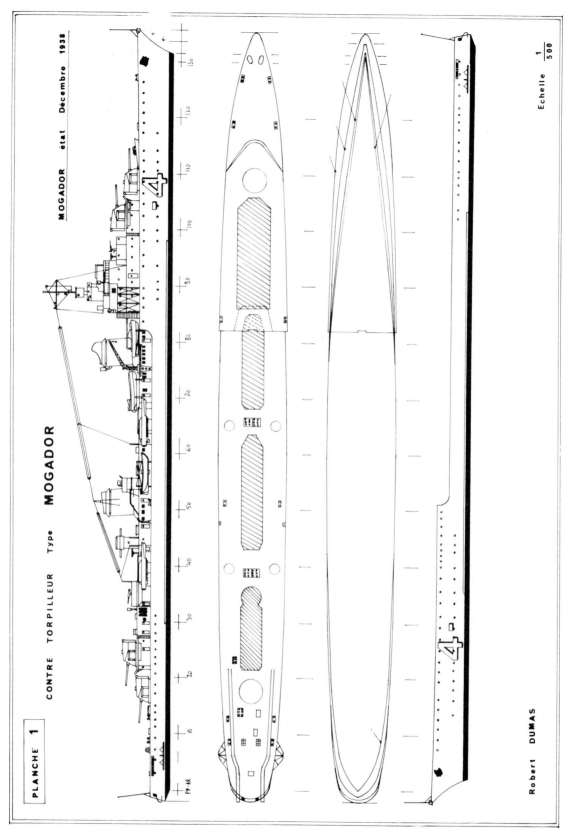

PLANCHE 1   CONTRE TORPILLEUR   Type   MOGADOR

MOGADOR   état   Décembre 1938

Echelle $\frac{1}{500}$

Robert DUMAS

Plan and elevation of *Mogador* in December 1938 as completed.
Robert Dumas

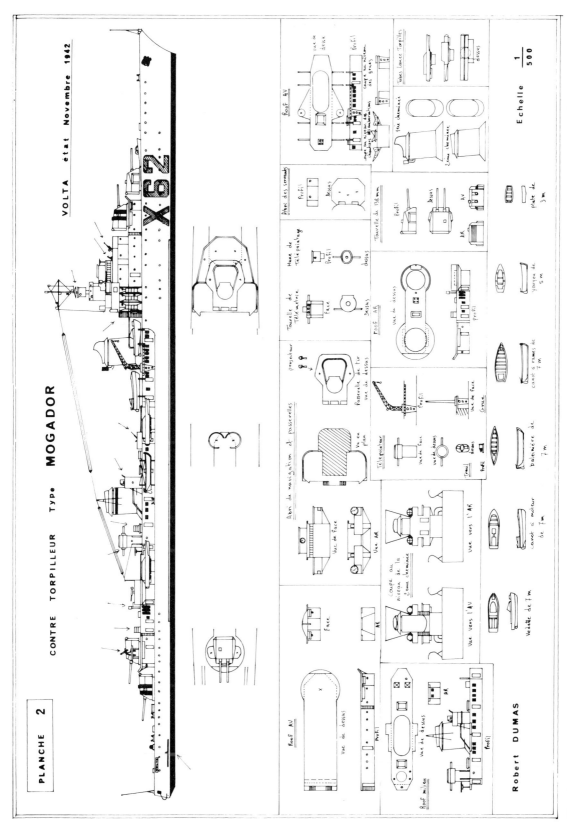

Elevation and superstructure details of *Volta* in her final guise,
November 1942.
Robert Dumas

Mogador scuttled and disarmed at Toulon November 1942. On her starboard side is the smaller and older *Guépard* class destroyer *Valmy*, one of 5 destroyers of that class to share their bigger consorts' fate. *Valmy* was refloated by the Italians and served as their *FR24* until scuttled again at Genoa.
Author's collection

the second funnel, the sign of the 6th Destroyer Division they belonged to. They had national Tricolour markings on the sides of Numbers 2 and 3 turrets (2 and 4 for *Volta* from the beginning of 1941).

OPERATIONAL HISTORY

From their entry into service *Mogador* and *Volta* formed the 6th Destroyer Division in the 2nd Light Squadron. This was part of the elite 1st Squadron of the Atlantic Fleet at Brest whose major ships were the battlecruisers *Dunkerque* and *Strasbourg* together with the cruisers *Georges Leygues*, *Montcalm* and *Gloire*.

The two destroyers escorted many British convoys bound for France during September and October 1939. From that date *Volta* underwent repairs at Brest. In November *Mogador* accompanied *Dunkerque* and HMS *Hood* in the hunt for *Scharnhorst* and *Gneisenau* and then escorted the Allied battlecruisers in the Atlantic approaches.

Both ships were with the Atlantic Fleet at Mers el Kebir (Oran) when it was attacked by Admiral Sir James Somerville's Force H on the evening of 3 July 1940. A British 15in shell hit *Mogador*, leading the six destroyers present ahead of *Strasbourg*'s breakout, in the stern and set off her depth charges, killing 38 of her crew. *Volta* escaped the tragic massacre with the four other destroyers and *Strasbourg* which they escorted towards Toulon where they arrived next day. *Volta*'s screening efforts included the long-range firing of torpedoes at *Hood*.

Mogador was put into a floating dock at Oran for temporary repairs. She left Mers el Kebir for Toulon in November 1940 under tow from the ocean tug *Laborieux*. Final repairs were made at Toulon.

Both destroyers were scuttled at Toulon among the 60-odd warships so denied the Axis on 27 November 1942. Though refloated by the Italians in mid-1943 neither was fit to be used and both wrecks were scrapped.

CONCLUSION

Mogador and *Volta* were the final stage in French destroyer construction. Like their immediate predecessors, the *Fantasque* class, they were given the heaviest possible main armament and the most powerful machinery to achieve extremely high speed. The French naval staff wanted to use them as raiding ships against enemy forces and coasts, but war experience revealed certain defects.

The 5.5in main armament was fragile and complicated. It was often in a damaged state that seriously restricted the rate of fire (normally 6rpm). The anti-aircraft armament was very limited and indeed French warships in general had inadequate air defence. This defect was partially remedied by adding 25mm and 13.2mm guns to *Volta*.

The French Navy was equally backward in anti-submarine warfare, lacking the Royal Navy's Asdic and powerful depth charge throwers. The latter weapon in French service was not very efficient.

Their radius of action was limited by insufficient oil fuel bunkers. That should not have been allowed in what were intended to be ocean escorts.

On the credit side their very solid construction should be mentioned. At Mers el Kebir *Mogador* survived a direct hit from a capital ship that exploded her depth charges as well. High speed was another asset as demonstrated by *Volta*'s escape from the carnage. This virtue had already been seen in three of the *Fantasque* class making a 35-knot sortie into and out of the Skaggerak during the Norwegian Campaign, surviving heavy air attack. *Mogador* and *Volta* had also previously showed their seaworthiness in the North Atlantic.

PROJECTED KLÉBER CLASS
To complete this study it is necessary to recall that France planned a modified and slightly larger *Mogador* class, the *Kléber*. Four destroyers were authorised, all

Volta scuttled at Toulon November 1942.
Author's collection

named after some of the Revolution's most dashing generals. *Kléber*, *Marceau* and *Desaix* came under the 1938 budget (vote of 2 May) and *Hoche* under that year's supplementary budget.

CHARACTERISTICS

Displacement	3750 tons normal, 4180 tons full load
Length overall	as *Mogador* class
Beam (maximum)	13.8/42ft 7in
Beam (waterline)	12.97m/42ft 7in
Draught	3.7m/12ft 2in forward, 4.65m/15ft 3in aft
Main armament	8 × 5.5in/45 Model 1934 guns in 4 twin mounts (35° elevation)
Anti-aircraft armament	4 × 4in/100mm Model 1930 guns in twin unpowered mounts able to elevate 80° 8 × 13.2mm Hotchkiss machine guns in four twin mounts
Torpedo tubes	6 × 550m/21.7in in two triple mounts
Oil	850 tons
Range	3600 miles at 20 knots
Other characteristics	as *Mogador* class

The Third Republic's last warship building programme, decreed on 1 April 1940, included six more super destroyers and it is almost certain that they would have been similar to the *Kléber* class. The names of two have been given as *Bruix* and *Bayard*.

BUILDERS

Kléber Ateliers et Chantiers de France at Dunkirk
Marceau Atliers et Chantiers de France at Nantes
Desaix Ateliers et Chantiers de France at Dunkirk
Hoche   Arsenal de Lorient

None of these ships had been laid down by the time of the armistice of June 1940. If France had not been conquered by Germany they would have entered service about 1943-44.

Volta in the Toulon area early in 1941.
Author's collection

Volta again in the Toulon area with her 1942 increased AA armament.
Author's collection

CONCLUSION

The *Kléber* class had important improvements in air defence, anti-submarine equipment and range (20 per cent more) over the *Mogador* class. And war experience would certainly have enhanced these additions. But these magnificent intended ships fell victim to that same war though it is interesting to note that their characteristics served as the point of departure for the *Surcouf* class cruiser escorts laid down from 1951 and still serving in the French Fleet.

ARKANSAS Class Monitors

by Frances J Allen

According to an article published in the *Scientific American* of December 1901; the *Arkansas* class of monitor was a direct result of 'panic legislation' itself caused by the Spanish-American War. The monitor was seen as solely a 'harbor defense vessel, and would be practically useless . . . in naval operations on the high seas'.[1]

In truth, however, the monitors that were acquired by the US Navy between the years 1898 and 1903, ten in all, were considered by many to be well suited to harbour defence and coastal protection. The notion that this was the correct and proper strategy for a Navy with ambitions to world power was also a contributing factor to the purchase of these ships described as a 'wallowing curiosity'.[2]

Five out of the ten monitors were 'holdovers from the Old Navy, twenty years in the building and constructed with iron hulls instead of steel'.[2] These were *Puritan* and four ships of the *Amphitrite* class. These new, yet ancient, warships had been started by the deceptive accounting procedure of using money earmarked for repairing Civil War monitors of the same names, to lay down new construction. The actual building of the vessels took an inordinately long time. This was a time of stagnation for America's armed forces and the Navy budget was no exception 'although considerable sums of

Sketch plan of US *Arkansas* class monitor, prepared by the Bureau of Construction and Repair, Navy Department.
US Naval Museum, Washington DC

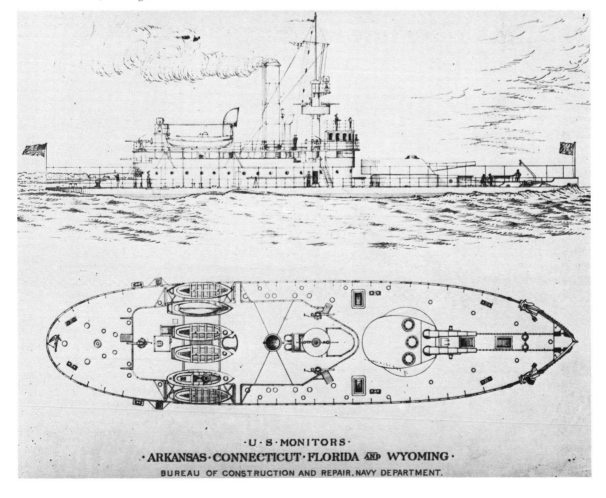

·U·S·MONITORS·
·ARKANSAS·CONNECTICUT·FLORIDA AND WYOMING·
BUREAU OF CONSTRUCTION AND REPAIR, NAVY DEPARTMENT.

USS *Arkansas* (BM7) 1906.
Library of Congress

money were dribbled into them under some cloudy constructual dealings'.[2]

With all of the dealings and long building schedules there was at least one benefit that was to be passed along to the later construction 'in 1887 armor requirements for them . . . four (monitors) were combined into a single order large enough to include United States industry to build the necessary steel forging and rolling facilities'.[2] This policy would result in some delays in the armour, but the Navy Department accepted this to be free of its dependency on foreign supplies.

It was by an act of 4 May 1898 that Congress appropriated the money for four monitors of a modern design. While the Navy was authorised to build double turreted monitors, they opted for a single turret design because of the limited available funds. The ships were to be of 3200-ton displacement and mount 12in rifle guns in fully balanced turrets, modern boilers and much electrically powered auxiliary machinery.

The new monitors were to be given state names just as battleships were. In 1908-9 these names would be exchanged for the names of cities in the state after which they were originally named.

Although these vessels were obsolete before they were even authorised, they did manage to render 'some contributions to naval progress . . . in 1908 the *Florida* . . . was employed as an experimental target in the Chesapeake Bay to determine the effects of modern large caliber projectiles and torpedoes on contemporary armour and hull construction. In another major experiment, the following year (1909), the West Coast

Monitor, *Cheyenne* (ex-*Wyoming*) was converted into the US Navy's first successful fuel oil-burning warship'.[2]

The single turreted monitors of the *Arkansas* class soldiered on into World War I and beyond. They were even used as submarine tenders 'although their low freeboard was about the only feature making them suitable for such a duty, *circa* 1913'.[2] Service was rendered by these ships as station ships, receiving and gunnery training vessels, militia and target ships.

The first decade of the twentieth century saw the use of *Arkansas, Florida, Nevada, Puritan* and *Terror* as Academy drill ships at the US Naval Academy, Annapolis, Maryland. During the 1920s all were sold as scrap except USS *Cheyenne*. This ship's 'modern engineering plant kept her on active Navy list until 1937 as a Naval reserve drill ship'.[2]

As the first of her class USS *Arkansas* is representative. She was built by Newport News Ship Building and Dry Dock Company from plans furnished by the Navy Department with the details to be worked out by the contractor. The price of $860,000 (about £172,000 at that period) was agreed upon minus boats, anchors, chains, armour and guns.

GENERAL ARRANGEMENT

'The hull was constructed of milled steel with transverse frames 3ft apart, special frames being worked in where necessary. The stem and stern posts are cast steel . . . the armour sits on a shelf and is 8in thick at midship and tapers to 4in thick forward and aft at waterline.'[3]

The ordnance authorised for *Arkansas* consisted of two 40-calibre 12in rifle guns in a balanced turret with traverse through 150° on each side; four 50-calibre 4in Mk 7 rapid firing rifles at corners of the superstructure; three 6pdr semi-automatic, four 1pdr Maxim-

USS *Florida* (BM9), *Arkansas* (BM7) and *Nevada* (BM8)
underway *c*1905.
US Naval Museum

USS *Florida* (BM9).
National Archives, Washington DC

1 USS *Tallahasee* (BM9) anchored in Hampton Roads on 10
December 1916, a few months before America's entry into
World War I. Alongside the monitor submarine tender are
two submarines *K-6* (SS37) and *K-5* (SS36).
US Naval Museum

2 USS *Arkansas* (BM7) coming down the Kenebech River to
Bath, Maine.
US Naval Museum

3 USS *Arkansas* being launched at the Newport News
Shipbuilding and Dry Dock Company, Newport News,
Virginia, on 10 November 1900.
US Naval Museum

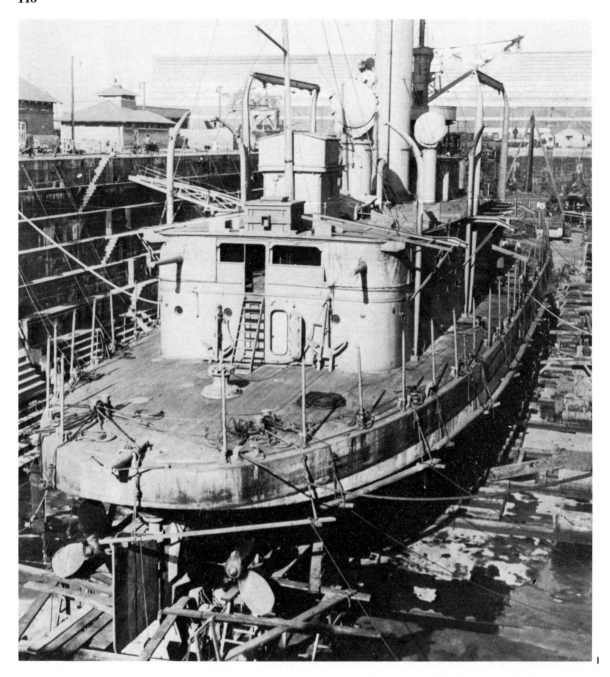

1 USS *Cheyenne* (BM10) in drydock at the Philadelphia Navy
Yard in December 1919.
US Naval Museum

2 USS *Florida* (BM9) fitting out at the Crescent Shipyard,
Elizabethport, New Jersey in 1901-2.
US Naval Museum

3 USS *Florida* (BM9).
US Naval Museum

2

3

USS *Wyoming* (BM10) off Mare Island Navy Yard, San Francisco, February 1903.
US Naval Museum

Nordenfeldt machine guns, a 1pdr rapid firing gun and two 6mm Colt automatics.

She carried four 28ft boats; a steam cutter, launch, whaleboat, and gig whaleboat. There were two 26ft cutters and an 18ft dinghy.

There were a total of eight ventilating systems on board and these were supplied by 11 fans, two powered by steam while the others were electric. Two fans for the forward system were in the dynamo room. They drew their air 'from ventilators in the hammock nettings and discharge through ducts leading forward on either side of the turret to all compartments forward of and including the dynamo room'.[3]

USS *Wyoming* (BM10) making 12.4 knots during her trials off San Francisco, California, in October 1902.
US Naval Museum

Two fans were also provided for the after system, one per shaft alley that fed all of the compartments on the berth deck abaft of the engine room. There was in addition to these a system for the steering engine room, a 70in fan and one No 5 Monogram fan in a main-deck system, two 70in fans for the engine room, a gravity system in the coal-bunkers, two steam fans in the after part of the boiler room for forced draft and finally the air spaces around the magazines were fed by the other fan systems.

The electrical plant was on the berth deck abaft the turret and forward of the firemen's wash room. For its day the system was well provided for, the engines and dynamos were supplied by General Electric Co. There were four dynamos of 32kw each. The main switchboard, the searchlight switchboard and the air compressor were located in the dynamo room. The turret was

trained by two 35hp motors and elevated by a pair of 3½hp units. The ammunition hoists were all electrically operated: two 3¾hp motors for the 4in ammunition hoist; two 12in hoists powered by a 20hp motor each; and the 3 and 6pdr ammunition hoist of 3¾hp each.

There were two searchlights using 50 volts and 70 amperes; eight 5-candlepower incandescent lamps; 249 of 15-candlepower; 10 32-candlepower with a total of 4344 candlepower.

Arkansas was provided with three sets of engines. The steering engine was manufactured by Williamson Bros Co of Philadelphia, and was capable of putting the helm amidships to hard-to-starboard in 13 seconds by use of a worm-and-screw-gear working the tiller. The Hyde Windless Co of Bath, Maine, built the anchor engines. This engine in official trials 'took in two anchors, weighing 5480lb starboard and 5130lb port with 114 fathoms of chain out at the rate of 6 fathoms per minute'.[3]

Placed abreast and in one watertight compartment were the main engines. These were three cylinder, triple expansion direct-acting. These engines were fed from four Thornycroft type, Daring pattern boilers, placed in

USS *Wyoming* (BM10); waves breaking over the ship's bow during her trials off San Francisco, California, in October 1902.

US Naval Museum

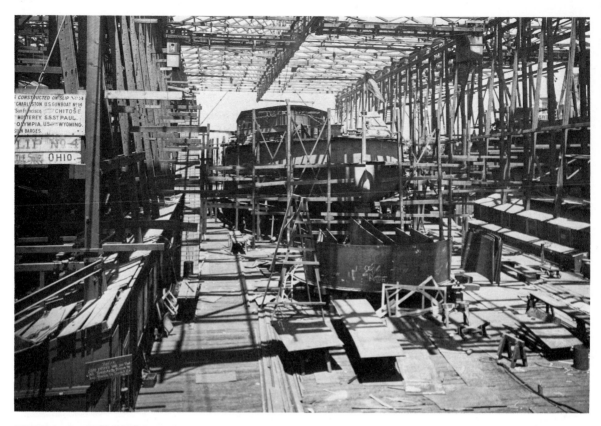

USS *Wyoming* (BM10) building at the Union Iron Works, San Francisco, California.
National Archives

USS *Wyoming* (BM10) showing her pre-1909 white paintwork and bow scroll decoration to advantage.

USS *Wyoming* (BM10) moored in West Coast waters before 1909.
US Naval Museum

one watertight compartment with the fire room running athwartships. 'Each boiler has one steam drum, three water drums and two furnaces ... The boilers were designed to carry a working steam pressure of 250lb.'[3]

This power train commanded twin screws of a modified Griffiths design. They were made of a manganese bronze compound. They were three bladed, adjustable pitch, right handed on starboard and left handed on the port side. The hubs were spherical, cut off at the ends.

'The standardization trials were made on the Barren Island course in the Chesapeake Bay, and the speed trials were run off Cape Henry in free route in the open sea. The bottom was clean and the vessel was in good condition. The coal was the New River, Collins Mine, hand picker. The draught during the trial was forward, 12ft 5¾in; aft, 12ft 9in; 12ft 7³⁄₁₆in.

The speed trials took place Tuesday, 7 August 1902 off Cape Henry, and the following data was taken. The run lasted two hours and the data was taken at half-hour intervals from 12.05 to 1.35pm.'[3]

REFERENCES

1 'Special Navy Issue-Development of the United States Navy Since the Spanish War,' *Scientific American* LXXXV (1901) pp373-90.
2 John D Alden, *American Steel Navy* (Naval Institute Press, Annapolis, Maryland, 1972).
3 Lt C K Mallory, USN, 'Description and Trials of US Monitor *Arkansas' Naval Engineers Journal* pp1172-85 (Vol 14 1902).

TABLE 1: GENERAL CHARACTERISTICS

Displacement	3200t (normal)
Length	252ft
Beam	50ft (max)
Draught	12ft 6in (mean)
Armament	2 × 12in/40 BL
	4 × 4in/50 QF
Armour	11in-5in (side)
	10in-9in (turrets) 7½in (CT)
Machinery	twin-screw vertical triple-expansion
Coal	350t
Speed	12.03kts; 1739ihp (*Arkansas*)
Complement	13 officers; 135 enlisted men

TABLE 2: SHIPS' HISTORIES (OUTLINE FORM)

USS *Arkansas*	Monitor No 7
Built	by Newport News Ship Building and Dry Dock, Co, Newport News, Virginia
Authorised	4 May 1898
Laid down	14 November 1899
Launched	10 November 1900
Commissioned	28 October 1902
Renamed *Ozark*	2 March 1909
Sold	26 January 1922
USS *Nevada*	Monitor No 8
Built	by Bath Iron Works, Bath, Maine
Authorised	4 May 1898
Renamed	from *Connecticut* during construction
Laid down	17 April 1899
Launched	24 November 1900
Commissioned	5 March 1903
Renamed *Tonapah*	2 March 1909
Sold	26 January 1922
USS *Florida*	Monitor No 9
Built	by Lewis Nixon, Elizabethport, New Jersey
Authorised	4 May 1898
Laid down	23 January 1899
Launched	30 November 1901
Commissioned	18 June 1903
Renamed *Tallahassee*	20 June 1908
Sold	25 July 1922
USS *Wyoming*	Monitor No 10
Built	by Union Iron Works, San Francisco, California
Authorised	4 May 1898
Laid down	11 April 1899
Launched	8 September 1900
Commissioned	8 December 1902
Renamed *Cheyenne*	1 January 1909
	Served as a Naval Reserve training ship 1920-1926
	Unclassified IX-4.
Stricken	25 January 1937
Sold	20 April 1939

Japanese 'Kaibokan' Escorts Part I

by Hans Lengerer

The term *Kaibokan* was introduced into the Imperial Japanese Navy by the Navy Ministry's communique No 34, dated 21 March 1898, which concerned the classification of major warships (*Gunkan*) and torpedo boats (*Suraitei*) (*Kantei ryubetsu*).[1] This term did not relate to a new type of ship; instead the new classification was to include the old cruisers and battleships whose fighting power was no longer up to the demands of the front line battlefleet, although still adequate for defensive service around the coasts of the home country. The new desig-

nation was an ideal reflection of their role, since the literal translation of *Kaibokan* is 'coastal defence ship'.

But the Japanese Navy did not possess armoured vessels of the coastal battleship type that had been specifically designed for coast defence duties by various navies up until the beginning of the twentieth century. This article does not, however, deal with these reclassified ships; instead it covers the vessels built under the name *Kaibokan*, principally as escorts. These ships were designed from the start as a new type of warship with

entirely different duties from earlier ships of that designation.

The idea of building these coast defence ships dates back to the period after the 1930 London Treaty. The Japanese Navy wanted to construct small coastal guardships under the name of *Kaibokan* (*Engan Keibikan*), intended for fishery protection and security tasks in the northerly Kurile islands, in order to circumvent the restricting regulations of this treaty. The Kuriles were in Japanese hands from 1875 to 1945 under the name Chishima. As a result of the strained financial situation, the plan could not be put into practice, as the funds had to be used for the building of higher priority ships. It was not until the Third Navy Armaments Extension Programme of 1937 that approval was granted for the construction of four ships under the designation *Kaibokan*. In further building programmes the Imperial Japanese Navy projected 364 ships, of which 167 had actually been completed by the end of the war. Together with the ships of the *Shimushu* class, a total of 171 ships were completed; 7 of them were commissioned by the Second

Disarmament Office (with approval of the American authorities) after the end of the war to carry out repatriation duties; in the case of 17 vessels, construction was stopped either early in 1945 or on 17 August 1945. The remaining 173 ships were cancelled. With a completed total of 171 ships, and 17 more laid down, the *Kaibokan* achieved the highest number of any one Japanese warship type constructed during the war. (They were only overtaken in the final phase of the war by a few special attack weapons and motor torpedo boats.)

The coastal defence ships were officially divided into Type A (*Ko*), C (*Hei*) and D (*Tei*), subdivided into the following classes: *Shimushu*, *Etorofu*, *Mikura* and *Ukuru* of Type A; *No 1* of Type C and *No 2* of Type D. However, if the ships are considered according to the changes made in their design, armament and equipment as a result of the many amendments, and in some cases complete redesigning, of the construction plans, then it seems more logical to divide them into the types to which they were allotted during initial planning. The *Shimushu* class is an exception here.

The result is the following arrangement:

Type A (*Ko*)	*Shimushu* class, *Etorufu* class
Type B (*Otsu*)	*Mikura* class
Modified Type B (*Kai Otsu*)	*Ukuru* class
Type C (*Hei*)	*No 1* class
Type D (*Tei*)	*No 2* class

The *Shimushu* class did not really belong to any type; it was conceived as the prototype of a new category of ship, but was in fact allotted to Type A, as were Types B and B Modified, and retained this classification. The only ships designed as Type A were the *Etorofu* class.[2]

Initially the coast defence ships were designed as multi-purpose vessels, with escort duties being regarded as only third priority. In the case of the *Etorofu* class, however, the design was altered to make convoy protection the most important role. Nevertheless in real terms convoy escort did not become the overriding requirement until the *Mikura* class, and if strict standards are applied, not until the *Ukuru* class. The desire for design simplicity, which had already led to the redesign of the *Etorofu* to *Ukuru* classes, had a decisive influence on later vessels. Prefabricated methods of mass production were regarded as necessary and this meant that the C and D Types were designed from the outset as cheap, single-purpose convoy escorts.

It should be remembered that although British corvettes and sloops were engaged in a life-or-death struggle with German U-boats in the Atlantic at this time, the Japanese Navy had virtually no comparable vessels. Even when Dönitz's early 1942 Operation *Paukenschlag* ('Drumbeat') against US East Coast shipping underlined the vulnerability of unescorted merchant ships, Japanese naval leaders gave no consideration for their own supply lines. The doctrine of the

The Kaibokan *Shimushu* (Type A) on trials in the Inland Sea June 1940 only 6 months after being launched by Mitsui.

126

TABLE 1: BUILDING PROGRAMMES IN WHICH KAIBOKAN WERE BUILT

Building programme	Building number	Type	Class	Planned	Built	Completed postwar	Building stopped	Stricken
Third Naval Armament Extension Programme of 1937 (budget for the financial year 1937)	9-12		Shimushu	4	4			
Fifth Naval Armament Extension Programme of 1942 (proposal for the financial year 1942)	750-793	Mod Class (Kai Gata)	Shimushu	4				4
Urgent war building programme for 1941 (budget for the financial years 1942 and 1943)	310-319 321, 323, 325, 330	A (Ko Gata)	Etorofu	14	14			
	320, 322, 324 326-329, 334	(Otsu Gata)	Mikura	8	8			
	331-333, 335-339	Mod B (Kai Otsu Gata)	Ukuru	8	8			
Modified Fifth Naval Armament Extension Extension Programme of 1942 (Special war budget of 1943)	5251-5284	Mod B (Kai Otsu Gata)	Ukuru	34	12		4	18
War Programme 1943-44 (Special war budget 1944-45)	4701-4721	Mod B (Kai Otsu Gata)	Ukuru	21	9			12
	2401-2532	C (Hei Gata)	No 1	132	53	3	9	67
	2701-2843	D (Tei Gata)	No 2	143	63	4	4	72
Totals				368	171	7	17	173

Notes
1 In the case of the *Mikura* and *Ukuru* classes, the type is that obtained at the time of initial planning.

2 The 'Planned' column only shows the ships included in a building programme. According to Fukui's *Japanese Naval Vessels at the End of the War* pages 71, 73, 75 there were further ships projected, as follows:

Ukuru class : approx 78 ships
No 1 class : approx 168 ships
No 2 class : approx 57 ships

The total number of ships planned (368) and of ships projected (approx 303) amounts to about 671.

The number of projected ships should be considered as unreliable, as the author has no further documentary evidence to confirm these figures.

decisive surface action, for which they constantly prepared, resulted in the neglect of all defensive tasks. This made a realistic assessment of the situation impossible, and the chance to take measures in good time against the US submarine menace was lost.

When the sinking of Japanese merchant ships by American submarines began to rise steadily, and the tanker losses en route from the vital South East Asian oil fields became critical, the countermeasures came too late. Priorities for anti-submarine vessels rose gradually from third in 1943 to first late in 1944, but even then the rate of production was inadequate. However, lack of numbers cannot entirely explain their low success rate against US submarines. Certainly the standard of Japanese sonar equipment and anti-submarine weapons was inferior to Allied equivalents, but the main reason was inadequate training. New ships were rushed into service without a proper work-up period, and whereas American submarines had had over two years to perfect their tactics, Japanese anti-submarine techniques had been almost entirely neglected. Furthermore towards the end of the war most Japanese escorts operated in areas where the US Navy had total mastery of the skies, or at least air superiority. In the circumstances, the failure of the Japanese anti-submarine forces, and the *Kaibokan* in particular, seems no more than inevitable.

TECHNICAL DESCRIPTION OF TYPE A, SHIMUSHU CLASS

The conditions of the London Treaty of 22 April 1930 imposed a total destroyer tonnage of 105,500 tons standard displacement on Japan (article 16). On 30 September 1930 Japan possessed 56 first class destroyers (totalling 75,125 tons) and 48 second class destroyers totalling 35,070 tons, ie a total of 104 ships with an aggregate displacement of 110,195 tons standard. Hence the construction of new destroyers was only possible if obsolete ships were replaced. However, article 8 paragraph (b) allowed the signatory powers to build surface vessels with a standard displacement of between 600 and 2000 tons, provided that they carried no guns larger than 155mm calibre, no more than 4 guns over 76mm calibre, no torpedo armament, and not more than 20 knots maximum speed. In consequence, Japan planned to build coast defence ships as a new type of vessel, to fill the space left by the urgently required destroyers. They were to have absolutely nothing in common with the ships earlier categorised as *Kaibokan*, and could be built in unlimited numbers in accordance with article 8 (b).

This is the reason why, in the first draft of the First Naval Armaments Extension Programme (*Dai ichi ji kaigun gunbi hoju keikaku*), which envisaged the construction of 117 warships of all types in two groups, four *Kaibokan* of 1200 tons standard displacement were included. The modified programme, reduced to 76 ships, contained the same number of *Kaibokan*, but with displacement reduced to 900 tons. Building costs were estimated at 9,380,000 Yen (a matter of £938,000 in precise contemporary terms), or 2,347,000 Yen (£234,700) per ship. Naval Minister Baron Kiyotane Abo proposed an alternative programme in secret document No 943, dated 7 October 1930, addressed to Prime Minister Yuko Hamaguchi; this was a reduced programme containing 59 ships, among them one coastal defence ship of 900 tons standard displacement, costing 2,100,000 Yen. But when the building programme was finally approved during the 59th session of parliament (26 December 1930 – 28 March 1931), under the abbreviated designation of First Programme (*Maru ichi keikaku*), it only included 39 ships: the coast defence ships had fallen prey to the finance minister's red pencil.

The first draft of the Second Naval Armaments Extension Programme (*Dai ni ji Kaigun gunbi joju keikaku*) again included four *Kaibokan* of 1200 tons standard displacement. The strategic/technical requirements were detailed in the appendix to secret document No 199 from the Admiralty staff, dated 14 June 1933. Speed was to be 20 knots, range more than 5000 miles at 14 knots. Four 127mm (5.1in) guns were the main armament, along with the required number of machine cannon, depth charges and depth charge throwers. When the programme was finally accepted during the 65th session of parliament (26 December 1933 - 26 March 1934) the fate of the first programme was repeated. The building programme, now known under the abbreviated title of Second Programme (*Maru ni keikaku*) contained only 48 ships instead of the proposed 88, and among that number were no coast defence ships.

After the renouncement of the Washington disarmament Treaty and the withdrawal of the Japanese delegation from the Second London Disarmament Conference, Japan became free of all treaty restrictions as of 1 January 1937. The reformulation of the national defence policy on 3 June 1936 was followed by the acceptance of the Third Naval Armament Extension Programme on 31 March 1937, during the 70th session of parliament (26 December 1936 - 31 March 1937). In this programme – the most extensive Japanese construction programme since the Washington Treaty of 6 February 1922 – the building of the four coastal defence ships, demanded since 1930, finally came about. Under the title of 'warships Nos 9-12' the third programme (*Maru san Keikaku*) covered the construction of four coastal defence ships. A total of 12,240,000 Yen (£1,224,000), or 3,060,000 Yen (£306,000) per ship and 2550 Yen (£255) per ton of displacement was the projected cost. In 1941 the budget was raised by just over 5% due to inflation, and the actual costs amounted to 12,866,112 Yen, or 3,216,529 Yen per ship/2680 Yen per ton of displacement.

A standard displacement of 1200 tons was stated on the budget. In fact the ships displaced only 860 tons, as a proportion of the funds was used for building the super battleships *Yamato* and *Musashi*. A further change was the replacement of the four 127mm AA guns in two twin mounts, required by the Naval General Staff, by three 120mm (4.7in) low angle guns. Speed was only 20 knots, while a range of 5000 miles at a speed of 16 knots was specified.

Except for the special duty warships (*Tokumukantei*), this was the first time that a major warship type was designed by a private yard. The basic plans were drawn up by Mitsubishi Heavy Industries warship design division. This design office had only been founded shortly before, to assist the Navy design department if it was overloaded or to draw up its own independent plan if foreign warship contracts were in prospect. Mitsubishi were granted the design contract because the Navy's design office was fully occupied with planning the great ships of the Third Programme (among them the super battleships *Yamato* and *Musashi* and the carriers *Shokaku* and *Zuikaku*). In any case the design of a ship destined for defensive tasks was considered unimportant.

One specification of the contract was that the ships should be suitable for use in the North Pacific as well as the South Seas and therefore had to be fitted out accordingly. The ships' principal role was as guardships (*Keibikan*) for patrol and fisheries protection in the Kuriles, so that the destroyers (*Kuchikukan*) hitherto entrusted with these duties could be released; the destroyers were not suited to this function and were urgently required to fulfil their real purpose. The secondary role was considered to be their use for minesweeping duties, and in third place came their use as escort

ships for convoys (*Sendan goeikan*); a task which later
became their principal purpose. Their final duty
included anti-submarine and anti-aircraft work. As with
gunboats, these ships were also intended for use during
periods of diplomatic tension. For this reason they were
to be built in such a way that they gave the appearance of
strong, battleworthy ships.

Although the Navy design office wanted a simple
design, the experienced team at Mitsubishi worked out a
very thorough, but complex design. The complicated
structure and equipment made prefabrication impossible, and extended building times considerably.
Although the design was far removed from a simple, fast
and easy-to-build ship, it was accepted under the basic
planning number E 15, principally because of the Navy's
low priority for these ships. In this way a design drawn up
to suit one set of duties became the prototype for a vessel
which had to carry out other escort duties. The initial
misplacing of priorities, combined with the insistence on
retaining an unsuitable design, had its inevitable effect
later; it was an important factor in the failure of Japanese anti-submarine warfare.

GENERAL ARRANGEMENT

At the planning stage the rough seas and the cold climate
of the North Pacific (Kuriles) were given special consideration, and great emphasis was placed on good stability
– even with an ice-covered superstructure, which would
raise the centre of gravity – along with structural
strength and good insulation. The required stability was

Shumushu in a peaceful anchorage early on in the Pacific War.
Her 10ft draught is being used to good advantage. The US
Office of Navy Intelligence thought she was part of an 8-ship
minelayer class but then reclassified her as a patrol frigate.
Author's collection

achieved by favourable weight distribution and construction methods, which resulted in a low centre of
gravity and a large metacentric height (the hull weight as
a proportion of the whole was 38% of the trials displacement). The inclusion of a forecastle deck ensured
adequate freeboard, which provided relatively good
seaworthiness (reserve buoyancy) and stability at large
angles of heel; the relatively large draught also helped in
these respects. The second requirement was met by making the hull plating 12mm ($\frac{1}{2}$in) thick at the waterline,
running from the bow to about half the length for protection against drifting ice and thin sheet ice), by the use of a
full-length double floor up to the level of the lower deck,
narrow frame compartments, and by the fitting of
mainhull members of appropriate strength for the
enormous stresses encountered in the North Pacific. The
third main requirement was approached by fitting a
powerful steam heating system, by providing for insulation and by designing the superstructure to allow movement from forward to aft inside the ship in poor weather
and with iced-up deck and superstructure. The two auxiliary boilers, used to drive the heating and auxiliary
machines, fed steam tubes that were used to melt the ice
from the anchor chains and to keep the windows of the
bridge ice-free. For the ships' use in warmer zones there
was adequate ventilation, and even a small air-
conditioning system.

With an overall length of 78m (255ft 11in) and maximum beam of 9.1m (29ft 10in) the ships displaced 860
tons standard. The machinery consisted of 2 Model 10
No 22 diesel engines (*22 go 10 gata*), of 4500bhp
(3310kW) with twin shafts, giving the ships a maximum
speed of 19.7 knots at 520rpm. The use of diesel engines
made it possible to achieve a considerable range of 8000
miles at 16 knots with 220 tons of fuel.

These and the following classes had a forecastle deck

TABLE 2: KAIBOKAN BUILDERS

YARD	Type / Class	A Shimushu	A Etorofu	B Mikura	mod B Ukuru	C No 1	D No 2	Completed or stopped postwar Ukuru	No 1	No 2	TOTAL
Fujinagata (Osaka)						3			1		4
Harima (Aioi)						10					10
Hitachi											
Mukojima (Mukajima)									(3)		(3)
Sakurajima (Osaka)			4	3	9					(2)	16 (2)
Ishikawajima (Tokyo)							4		1 (1)		5 (1)
Kawasaki											
Kobe Shipbuilders							5				5
Senshu (Tanagawa)							4		2		6
Kyowa (Kobe)								(3)			(3)
Maizuru DY						3					3
Sasebo DY		1			4						5
Yokosuka DY							6				6
Mitsubishi						10		(2)			10 (2)
Kobe											
Nagasaki							31				31
Mitsui Shipbuilders											
Tamano		2	4		5						11
Naniwa Dock (Osaka)						3					3
Nihonkai Dock Industry (Toyama)						6		(2)			6 (2)
Niigata Iron Works						4		(1)			4 (1)
Nippon Steel Tube Co											
Tsumi (Yokohama)		1	2	5	4	27			3 (1)		42 (1)
Uraga Dock											
Uraga (Yokosuka)			4		7			(2)			11 (2)
TOTALS		4	14	8	29	53	63	(4)	3 (9)	4 ()4	171 +
					177				7 + (17)		7 + (17)

TABLE 3: ANNUAL KAIBOKAN DELIVERIES

Class	1940	1941	1942	1943	1944	1945	Total
Shimushu	3	1					4
Etorofu				13	1		14
Mikura				2	6		8
Ukuru					14	15	29
No 1					36	17	53
No 2					44	19	63
Totals	3	1		15	101	51	171

with a curved hancing piece. In the case of the *Shimushu* class, the length of the forecastle (or superstructure) deck was about 23m (75ft 6in). It had a slight sheer and at the deck step the odd angular shape also characteristic of *Hatsutaka* class minelayers and also contemporary destroyer classes (*Fubuki, Hatsuhara, Kagero* and so on). The bow shape was also typical of Japanese ships of this period, curved into a gentle 'S' shape with a large overhang at the stem. There was a short gap between the deck step and the superstructure that extended to the after part of the ship. This allowed internal movement fore and aft, thus reducing the danger for the crew of working on the exposed and sometimes frozen upper deck.

The forward end of the bridge was enclosed but the bridge windows allowed all-round visibility. The open platform above it was dominated by an enclosed 3m (39in) rangefinder with an 8cm (3.1in) binocular sight forward. The rear, open part of the bridge extended almost as far aft as the tripod foremost. A lookout position was fitted at the upper end of the supporting legs, which were raised aft. The topmast also carried yards for signal halliards, wind direction indicator, anemometer, signal lamps and so on. Two forward-raking yards carrying the radio aerials, completed the top-hamper. Between the tripod mast and a platform carrying a 75cm (30in) searchlight was the radio direction finder. Abaft the searchlight platform came the funnel, which was raked aft. The upper part was reduced in cross-section above the level of the searchlight, in order to increase the illumination arc aft. The galley funnel, angled forward at the top, ran along the after side of the funnel and finished just above the latter. The shorter, tripod mainmast was raked strongly backwards and was somewhat farther distant. The tripod foremast's vertical arrangement and the yards' forward rake allowed longer radio aerials, since the mainmast's yards were again forked aft, in similar fashion to those of the *Yamato* class battleships. The engine room ventilators were located abreast the foremast.

ARMAMENT

The main armament consisted of three 12cm/45 (4.7in) low angle guns of the Year 3 type (*3 nendo shiki*) introduced into the Japanese Navy in 1914; they had an elevation of only 33° in the Type G mounting. These were the same weapons as were mounted, for example,

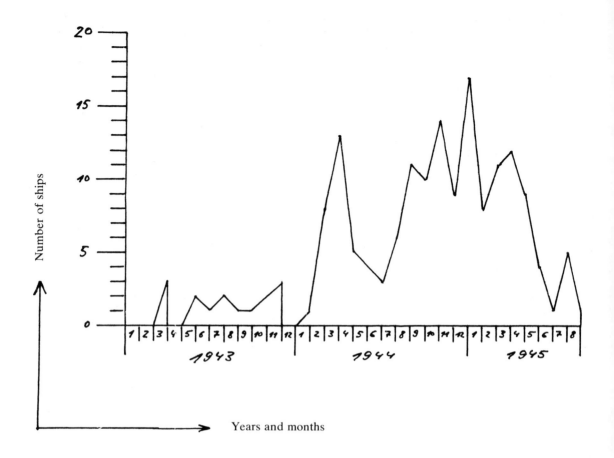

Number of ships

Years and months

on the *Mutsuki* class old destroyers. They were disposed on the centreline, with one forward of the bridge, and two aft (one on the superstructure deck). Careful consideration was given to the effects of blast, and all three were given wide arcs of fire.

Four 25mm automatic guns were provided for anti-aircraft defence, in two twin mounts on platforms to port and starboard of the bridge at the superstructure deck level. A practice gun was fitted abaft the after 12cm mount, along with a Model 94 (1934)[3] depth-charge thrower and a Model 3 loading frame. Three depth-charge launchers were mounted on each side of the quarterdeck right aft, and 18 Model 95 depth charges were carried.[4] The installation of hydrophones and sonar equipment was planned, but this class was completed without them. Minesweeping gear was carried abreast the superstructure 12cm gun platform, and a cutter and a motor boat, both 6m (19ft) long, were slung in swivelling davits each side of the funnel.

REDESIGNATION AND REARMAMENT 1942-44
Until 1 July 1942 the coast defence ships were classified as major warships (*Gunkan*). On this date the *Kaibokan* were removed from the list of *Gunkan* by secret order

No 1186, and the type was reintroduced as minor warships (*Kantei*) coming next after the submarines (*Sensuikan*).[5] The official communication No 192 (for naval circles only), also dated 1 July 1942, altered the classification from *Gunkan* to *Kaibokan*. The old armoured cruisers (*Junyokan*), *Yakumo*, *Iwate*, *Izumu*, at this time still classified as *Kaibokan*, were reclassified as first class cruisers (*Itto Junyokan*); their contemporaries *Asama*, *Azuma*, *Kasuga* were reclassified as special duty warships (*Tokumukan*).

Designating the *Shimushu* class as *Kaibokan* required them to be treated as major warships. The Imperial crest, the chrysanthemum, was fitted at the bow; it was made of wood, had a diameter of 450mm (16in) and was gilded. The captain's quarters consisted of an audience room and a sleeping cabin, as on the larger gunboats. In the audience room (to starboard, at the forward gun position) hung the portrait of the Emperor and Empress. The captain, despite the small displacement of his ship, was a Commander or a Captain*, simply because of the ship's classification. Nevertheless, when a destroyer was met, no salute was fired, although she would be commanded by a Lieutenant Commander or at best a Commander. Putting *Shimushu* in the ship's classification list as a 'Mini-Kaibokan' when her principal duty was to protect whaling ships, had in fact led to some disquiet, as the other coastal defence ships were large; especially as her displacement had been stated incorrectly in the list as 8600 tons.

The thorough design resulted in a ship with a satisfactory performance, although the design was certainly too complex, and 90,000 man-days of 8.5 hours each were required for hull construction alone. The long building time was the greatest problem, and it was only from the *Ukuku* class onward that good results were obtained. The *Shimushu* is a good example of how the Japanese dictum 'quality before quantity' could have most unfortunate results in practice.

After the outbreak of war all four ships of the *Shimushu* class were sent to the North Pacific. In 1942 a Model 93 sonar unit (1933)[6] was installed, and the

number of depth charges was doubled (to 36). One year later this was increased again (to 60). The depth-charge launchers on either side of the stern were removed and replaced by launching rails. At the same time the fitting of Type 22 radar also began, the aerials being fitted on the foremast, which was modified accordingly, and fitted with a platform. From autumn 1944 the ships were fitted with a Type 13 radar set, whose fixed aerial was mounted on the mainmast.

After the Battle of the Philippine Sea (18-22 June 1944) extensive augmentation of anti-aircraft weapons was carried out on all Japanese ships. The *Shimushu* class carried 15 25mm machine guns in five triple mounts after this refit. The twin mounts were replaced by triples, and two further triples were installed on platforms between the funnel and mainmast on either side of the superstructure deck. A further AA bandstand for the fifth triple was fitted at the extreme end of the forecastle. In addition the bridge was extended forward and an 80mm (3.1in) Army mortar was installed there.

Shimushu was hit by a torpedo from the US submarine *Haddo* in the western half of Manila Bay on 25 November 1944, and her bow blown off. During the repair the simplified bow form of that period was fitted, so at the end of the war the ship had a straight stem. The *Schimushu* class numbered four ships, of which one was sunk during the war.

As a result of the satisfactory performance of these ships, and the urgent need for escort ships, the plans were altered only slightly to build the *Etorofu* class.

To be continued

TABLE 4: SHIMUSHU CLASS TECHNICAL DETAILS

Basic planning number	E15
Number built	9
Standard displacement	860 tons
Trial displacement	1020 tons
Length between perpendiculars	72.5m/237ft 11in
Waterline length	76.2m/250ft
Overall length	77.7m/255ft
Waterline beam	9.1m/29ft 10in
Side height	5.3m/17ft 5in
Average draught	3.05m/10ft
Machinery	2 No 22 type 10 diesels (4500bhp)
Speed	19.7kts
No of propellers and rpm	2 × 520rpm
Fuel	220 tons
Range	8000nm/16kts
Armament	3 × 12cm/45
	4 × 25mm
	18 Mod 95 depth charges
	Mod 94 thrower
	Mod 3 loading frame
Additional armament	11 × 25mm
	8cm army mortar
Sensors	Type 13 radar
	Type 22 radar
	Sonar
Crew (according to budget)	147

NOTES

1 Below the category of cruisers (*Junyokan*) three different classes of coastal defence ships were registered as follows: first class ships of more than 7000 tons, second class of between 7000 tons and 3500 tons, third class of under 3500 tons normal displacement. As early as 28 August 1912 there was a change to a two-class division, with the first class over 7000 tons and the second below. In this connection it is worth mentioning that before the term *Kaibokan* was introduced, the 'three ships of the finest landscapes', the protected cruisers *Itsukushima*, *Matsushima* and *Hashidate* were designated as coastal defence ships during the Sino-Japanese War of 1894-95
2 These data are based on table 2 ('Naval building programmes in the Sino-Japanese conflict until the Second World War') in Shizuo Fukui's book *The Japanese Warships* (*Nihon no gunkan*), and in the text of the book on page 146. Other designations are not accurate, as Fukui, writing of the *Etorofu* type, writes 'this ship, classified as Class A, began . . .'. This state-

TABLE 5: SHIMUSHU CLASS OUTLINE

Running no	Building no	Name	Builder	Laid down	Launched	Completed
1	9	*Shimushu*	Mitsui, Tamano	29.11.38	13.12.39	30. 6.40
2	10	*Kunashiri*	Tsurumi	1. 3.39	6. 5.40	3.10.40
3	11	*Hachijo*	Sasebo DY	3. 8.39	10. 4.40	31. 3.41
4	12	*Ishigaki*	Mitsui, Tamano	15. 8.39	14. 9.40	15. 2.41

Notes
1 Repatriation, laid up Maizuru. To USSR 5.7.47 as *Nachhodka*.
2 Repatriation, wrecked off Omaezaki 4.6.46. Hull above surface, BU Japan.
3 Out of action at Maizuru 15.8.45, BU 5.4.48 by Ino, Maizuru.
4 Sunk 31.5.44 US Submarine *Herring* (70nm W of Matsuwa island - Kuriles)

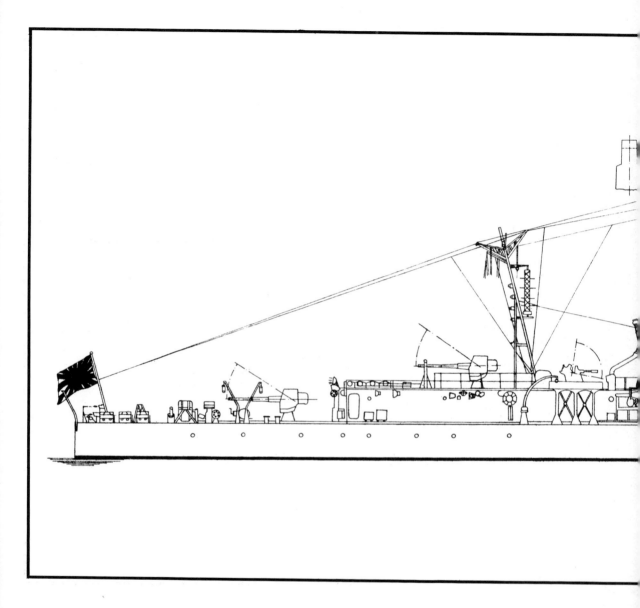

Sketch 1 Type A, *Shimushu* class; *Shimushu* after receiving a strengthened AA armament, less minesweeping equipment and with the bow of the Type C, which she received after being torpedoed in the Philippines on 25 November 1944.
Small sketch, right Original form of the bow on *Shimushu*.
Small sketch, left Section through the funnel of the *Shimushu* class. *Shimushu* was fitted with the funnel of the *Etorofu* class during the repair.

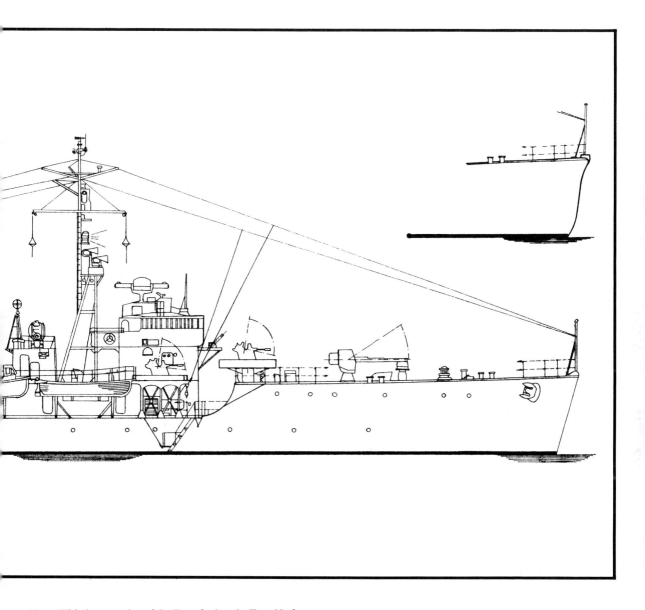

Note: With the exception of the *Etorofu* class the Type No 2, the sketches in this series are based on photographs of the coastal defence ships published to date. As most of these have been taken at an oblique angle, which is not exactly ideal for measurements, the draughtsman/artist has been forced to estimate dimensions. This is especially true of the small sketches.

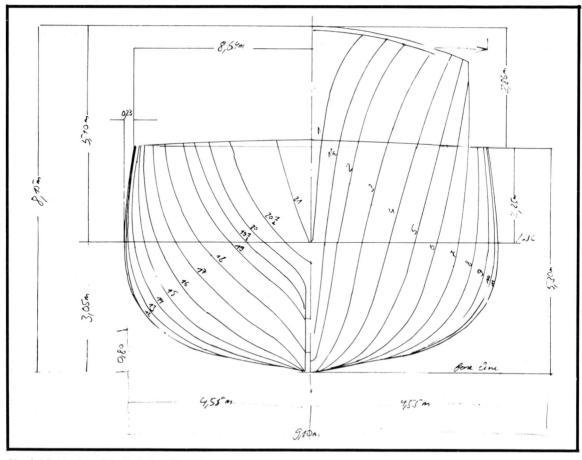

Sketch 2 Body plan of the Kaibokan *Shimushu*

ment agrees with Fukui's *'Japanese naval vessels at the end of the War'*, p69-71, *Sekai no kansen* No 4/1959 p8-10, and 12/1966 p6-7, *History of shipbuilding in the Showa period — before and during the War (Shava Zosenshi-Senzen, Senji)*, Vol 1 p565 and Seiji Higashi's 'History of changes to the *Kaibokan* in drawings' in *Maru Special* No 28 p 20-31.

3 The Model 94 depth-charge thrower had been introduced in September 1934 as standard weapon in the Japanese Navy under the designation 'Type Y launching device, depth-charge twin launching device'. It would be used either as a single-side thrower, or for both sides simultaneously. Two firing tubes in the form of a Y at 50° inclination ran from the central part. The width, measured from the outside edge to the outside edge of the tubes, was 1.484m, the height from the base plate to the top of the centre part 1.083m. The floor area of the base late was 90cm × 50cm (35in × 20in). The thrower weighed 680kg (1500lb). When using the Model 95 (1935) depth charge, the depth charges could be hurled a distance of 75m (246ft) with simultaneous firing. The duration of flight was then 4.5 seconds. With a single firing, the range became 105m (344ft 6in) with 5.0 seconds flight duration. The Model 95 (1935) depth charge had a cylindrical shape. It was 77.5cm (2ft 6in) long, 45cm (16in) in diameter, and its all-up weight of 160kg (325lb) included 100kg (220lb) of Type 88 explosive. The sinking speed was around 1.9m or 6ft a second. Detonation depths of 30m (98ft), 60m (196ft) and 90m (295ft) could be set.

4 In contrast to the figure of 12 depth charges stated on p69 of 'Japanese Naval Vessels at the end of the War', Fukui states 18 depth charges on p20 of his book '*The Japanese Warships*', (published later), and the same number in table 9 of the appen-

dix to this book. This also agrees with the information on coastal defence ships in *Sekai no kansen* 7/1959, p51, and with the two sources named in note 2.

5 The classification *Gunkan* was a sub-division of the large section *Kantei*. In 1945 the following ships were classed as primary warships:
Battleships (*Senkan*)
Aircraft carriers (*Kokubokan*)
Cruisers, first and second class (*Itto* and *Nito Junyokan*)
Seaplane carriers (*Suijokibokan*)
Submarine tenders (*Sensuibokan*)
Minelayers (*Fusetsukan*)
Training battleships (*Renshusenkan*)
Training cruisers (*Renshujunyokan*)
The ships belonging to the *Gunkan* did not carry their normal class designation, but were designated *Gunkan*.

6 The Model 93 (1933) Sonar was installed in ships of the Third Programme and later. This was an active device. The soundwaves were transmited by a piezo-electric transmitter and then picked up again. The shortest locating distance with a submarine at a depth of 30m (98ft) was 200m (656ft). This figure rose to 250m (820ft) at a depth of 60m (196ft), and to 400m (1312ft) at a depth of 100m (328ft). On CD 22 (CD = symbol for *Kaibokan*) the following figures were given as longest locating ranges for a submarine travelling at 7.5 knots:
Own speed 0 knots = 4200m (4592yds)
Own speed 12 knots = 3000m (3280yds)
Own speed 14 knots = 1800m (1968yds)
These figures illustrate that the capability of the device deteriorated very rapidly when its own speed was raised.

British Naval Guns 1880-1945 No.13

by N J M Campbell

6in BL Mk XXII This rather heavy 50 calibre gun was internally similar to the much more widely used Mk XXIII. It was developed for the G3 battlecruisers and was mounted from 1927 in the battleships *Nelson* and *Rodney*. The gun was of normal taper wound wire construction with a hand operated Welin screw breech block and when new had no inner A tube and was known as Mk XXII*. On lining with a tapered inner A tube it became Mk XXII. Some years later Mk XXII** was introduced and this had inner A and A tubes but no wire. In all 40 guns were made including 2 experimental prototypes, and of the total 6 were Mk XXII**.

Originally 100lb shells were fired but from about 1942 112lb were used as in Mk XXIII. The Mk XVIII twin mounting allowed + 60° to − 5° elevation with loading at + 5°. It was hydraulically powered from a self-contained unit and had powered rammers but the rate of fire was slow at 5rpm. Flash precautions were very thorough. Revolving weight was *c*85 tons with a 14ft mean roller path dia.

6in BL Mk XXIII Introduced from 1933 in *Leander* this gun was mounted in all subsequent 6in cruisers up to and including *Superb* in 1945. It was also intended for the *Tiger* class as originally designed, and but for the war would have been adopted as a heavy field gun after years of Army indecision. The Mk XXIII was built with A tube, jacket to 115in from the muzzle, breech ring and breech bush screwed into the jacket. The Welin screw breech block had a hand-operated Asbury mechanism. On lining with a tapered inner A tube the gun was known as Mk XXIII*, the reverse nomenclature to that of Mk XXII. A modified gun with power worked breech mechanism was intended for the quadruple turrets originally proposed for the *Belfast* class and was to be Mk XXIV, but this mark was later adopted as a coast defence gun. In all 469 Mk XXIII were made.

The *Leander*, *Perth* and *Arethusa* classes had twin Mk XXI mountings, the *Southampton* and *Gloucester* classes triple Mk XXII and later cruisers from the *Belfast* class to the *Superb* triple Mk XXIII, with the triple RP10 Mk XXIV in the *Tiger* class as originally designed. This last was to have 60° elevation but otherwise generally resembled Mk XXIII apart from RPC. Mk XXI and XXII were short trunk turrets and XXIII long trunk. All 3 had hand ramming and were otherwise powered by a self-contained hydraulic system. The rate of fire was 6-8rpm and preferred loading angle + 7° to + 5°.

Mounting	Elevation	Loading	Rev Weight	Mean Roller Path dia
XXI	+60°−5°	+12½°−5°	95 tons	13ft 9in
XXII	+45°−5°	+12½°−5°	150/155 tons	19ft
XXIII	+45°−5°	+12½°−5°	175 tons	19ft

6in BL Mk XXIV An Army coast defence gun with the same performance as Mk VII* (100lb shell, MV 2890fs) but built with a loose barrel. It is believed that about 140 were made in World War II.

6in N5 This gun originally known as 6in QF Mark V, was developed from 1944 after some abortive work in 1942-43. It was clear that a 6in BL gun had become an anachronism and that any new design should be QF with separate ammunition loaded at one rammer stroke. It was originally intended for triple 80° elevation Mk XXV turrets in the projected *Neptune* class and then for the twin Mk XXVI in the *Minotaur* class designs of 1947. These were in turn abandoned and the first two experimental guns were not completed until 1949.

After extensive trials ashore and in the trials cruiser *Cumberland* the N5 in a modified Mk XXVI twin turret was eventually introduced in *Tiger* completed in March 1959, 15 years after the start of the gun's development. It was also in her sister ships *Blake* and *Lion*.

In its final form it was a loose barrel gun with hydraulically operated horizontal sliding breech block, and steel cartridge cases replaced brass. The staff requirement of continuous fire at 20rpm could be met but the muzzles in particular got excessively hot and water cooling had to be used. The 2 guns in a turret were not fixed together.

The mountings allowed 78½° (?80°) elevation with power loading at any angle, and 3 of those afloat had RP15 hydraulic control and 3 RP53 electric. It is believed that initially at least the turrets in *Tiger* and one in *Lion* had hydraulic control and the other in *Lion* and those in *Blake* electric.

5.5in BL Mk I Designed by Coventry Ordnance Works for Greece, this gun was introduced with the former Greek light cruisers *Birkenhead* and *Chester* and was adopted for further manufacture in 1914-18; 246 guns were ordered including those taken over, but only 81 were actually completed. It was of normal wire wound contruction with a tapered inner A tube and Welin screw block with Holmstrom mechanism, and was mounted in *Hood*, *Furious*, *Hermes*, *Birkenhead*, *Chester* and *K17* though not in other 'K' class submarines for which it was

Southampton's Mk XXII triple 6in 'Y' turret is hoisted on
board by John Brown's 150-ton hammerhead crane at their
Clydebank shipyard on 3 July 1936. The turrets were usually
delivered by coaster from Vickers-Armstrong's works, Barrow
supplying west coast yards and Elswick east coast.
Upper Clyde Shipbuilders/courtesy of Ian Buxton

PARTICULARS OF 6in GUNS

	6in BL Mk XXII	6in BL Mk XXIII
Weight inc BM (tons)	9.0125 (XXII** 9.023)	6.906
Length oa (in)	309.728	309.8
Length bore (cals)	50	50
Chamber (cu in)	1750	1750
Chamber length (in)	40.809	41.0
Projectile (lb)	100	112
Charge (lb/type)	31 SC150	30 SC150
Muzzle Velocity (fs)	2960	2758
Range (yds)	25,800/45°	25,480/45°

	6in N5	5.5in BL Mk I
Weight inc BM (tons)	c6.85	6.230
Length oa (in)	c315	284.728
Length bore (cals)	50	50
Chamber (cu in)	c1720	1500
Chamber length (in)	47	36.46
Projectile (lb)	129.75	82
Charge (lb/type)	34.5 MNF2P/S 224-058	22.54 SC115, 22.25 MD19
Muzzle Velocity (fs)	2513	2790
Range (yds)	25,330/42.7°	17,770/30°

originally intended. During World War II it was also in
the AMCs *Laurentic* and *Montclare* and in emergency
coast defence batteries.

There were a number of different transferable mountings:

Mounting	Elevation	Ships
PI	+15° −7°	*Birkenhead, Chester*
PI*	+25° −7°	*Furious, Hermes, Laurentic, Montclare*
PI**	+25° −7°	*K17*
CPII	+30° −5°	*Hood*

Elevation in *K17* may have been limited to 20° by height
above deck.

5.5in BL Mk II A 42 calibre gun intended for World War
I DAMS, which did not get beyond the design stage,
though it had been intended to build 1100. New guns
would have been Mk II* with an A tube, taper wire and
full length jacket, becoming Mk II on lining with an
inner A tube. Weight without BM would have been
5.625 tons. Later 5.5in BL Marks were Army gun-
howitzers of World War II.

Bermuda receives her Mk XXIII triple 6in 'A' turret at
Clydebank on 11 May 1942. Note the roller path supporting
the final 157-ton revolving weight. The roof plates will only be
fitted after the guns have been shipped.

Upper Clyde Shipbuilders/courtesy of Ian Buxton

BOOK REVIEWS

THE SHIP OF THE LINE, VOLUME 1
The development of the battlefleet 1650-1850 by Brian Lavery
Published by Conway Maritime Press October 1983
224pp (30cm × 25cm) 110 illustrations, 18 line drawings and 8 graphs, index
ISBN 085177 252 8 (£20)
There has not been a full coverage of the British sailing ship of the line since John Fincham's History of Naval Architecture in 1851. That book was inadequate in its treatment of the earlier years relying too much on the prejudiced views of John Charnock. Brian Lavery has spent many years in his research and has published several important articles on sailing warships as well as editing the Conway edition of *Deane's Doctrine of Naval Architecture*.

The Ship of the Line Volume 1 traces the development of the ship of the line against the background of political and economic pressures. Operational history is only covered in sufficient depth to show how experience in war was used to influence future designs.

The graphs are particularly valuable in showing how the various categories of ship grew in size, altered in characteristics and often supplanted the next rate above. Despite the subtitle, there is fairly full coverage from 1588 onwards. In these earlier years the debate was between 'high charged' and 'low charged' ships. By the mid-seventeenth century there was argument concerning the relative numbers of two and three deckers.

The early years of the eighteenth century were an unfortunate period for British ship design, confined by the straightjacket of the establishment rules and by the concept of rebuilding. It is interesting to read that ships dismantled for rebuilding were still listed even when they had been no more than piles of used timbers for years. The appointment of Sir Thomas Slade as Surveyor in 1755 followed soon after by Admiral Lord Anson's return to the Board of Admiralty led to a more successful era.

The ships of the French Revolutionary Wars were fully up to their job. The British three deckers were very good as were most of the 74s. The Royal Navy fell behind the French in the introduction of the big two decker of 80 guns. This was probably due to lack of resources in timber and in shipbuilding labour though the topic is not fully explored.

There are some inadequate treatments of technical matters. For example, on page 94, it is said that the

74-gun *Invincible*, a 1747 prize from the French, had a speed of 13 knots compared with 11 for British ships. The condition of wind and bottom state are not given and, if all else was equal, an extra two knots speed implies some 65% more power (or reduction of resistance). This could only be explained by the effects of fouling.

Sir Robert Sepping's pioneer work on the development of timber structures is not given the credit it deserves and this reviewer finds the comment on page 149 that Seppings was 'an engineer rather than a naval architect' impossible to understand. One hopes that Volume II will cover the structural characteristics of wooden hulls more fully.

It should be brought out that much of Seppings' work was inspired by the acute shortage of big timbers for shipbuilding. His structural style enabled effective use to be made of short pieces. Seppings used iron diagonals in frigates and this was extended to the battlefleet by Edye, Sir William Symonds' professional assistant.

The main text of the book finishes at page 156 and is followed by an invaluable set of annexes. First, there are 35 pages of ship lists giving build particulars of all line of battle ships from 1618, divided into classes.

Then follow detailed appendices on numbers, specifications, armament and dimensions as well as two or three big documents reproduced in full. The references are fully documented and anyone wishing to challenge the author's views will have a great deal of reading to do.

At last, we have a real reference book for the ships that won British supremacy at sea and led to the creation of the British Empire.

D K Brown

OTHER BOOKS RECEIVED
Victoria's Navy: The heyday of steam by Colin White (Kenneth Mason, October 1983) 176pp, 220 prints and photographs, index, £11.95, ISBN 0-84937-284-7, 10in/24.5cm × 7in/18cm. The companion and follow up volume to the same author's *The end of the sailing navy* (Kenneth Mason, 1980) for which see the full review in *Warship* 20 by D K Brown. The index is for both volumes, format and chapter topics being identical. The evocative Victorian and Edwardian illustrations, almost all from the RN Museum, Portsmouth (of which the author is now deputy director), are the essence of this

book, the text being no more than an outline link for the period 1870-1910. For a pictorial book, full of nostalgic *Illustrated London News* engravings in particular, the captions really should have been more detailed and this editor for one cannot see why Victorian lacks its initial capital letter. Pedantry apart this is an appealing synthesis of the period with a welcome emphasis on sailors as well as ships, not least the original Player's Navy Cut seaman from the 1885 turret ship HMS *Hero*.

Destroyer! German Destroyers in World War II by M J Whitley (Arms and Armour Press, October 1983) 310pp, 44 photographs, 14 maps, 15 line drawings, 7 appendices, bibliography, index, £12.95, ISBN 0-85368-258-5, 9in/22.8cm × 6in/15cm. This subject receives the exhaustive and infinitely painstaking treatment from an author well known to readers of *Warship*. See the publisher's advertisement in issue 29 for a full listing of battle plans and drawings included (limited by the format and not therefore fully detailed) though the book is 310pp long not 336pp. Even the dustjacket is used to illustrate camouflage schemes. The first and surely the last English language history of Hitler's 40 powerful but flawed destroyers, the first third of the book covers design and construction before a chronological account of their many varied and often little known operations. The maps and action tracks, enhanced by silhouettes of the participating ships, are pleasing to the eye though they lack scales. The technical appendices list the statistics (metric only) and summarise the careers of all the ships. One can think of only two omissions from this excellent work, there is no personal quotation from destroyer men or any discussion of the signal failure of 4th Flotilla (5 destroyers) to stay with *Scharnhorst* on Boxing Day 1943.

Le Porte-Avions Arromanches 1942-1978 by René Bail and Jean Moulin (Charle-Lavauzelle, Paris-Limoges, 1983) 92pp, 162 photographs and plans, no index, bibliography, 12in/30cm × 9in/22.5cm, 119 francs (approx £10). First of a pictorial 'Vie des Navires' series devoted to the light fleet carrier HMS *Colossus* which became France's *Arromanches* in 1946 serving until 1974 and broken up in 1978. Captions in English and French of carrier operations, especially Indochina 1948-54 and Suez 1956, and a look at her 8 sister ships.

A's & A's

GERMAN NAVAL RADAR (*Warship* 21, 22 and 27)
From Erwin Sieche, Vienna, Austria
Warship-reader Michael Bullen has found in his personal collection some pictures and plans of German naval radar equipment, thus adding new facts to the above mentioned theme:

Tirpitz: the Drüppel photographs RM 794 and RM 3752 clearly show that she also carried the huge FuMO 26 on the forward rangefinder tower since spring/summer 1944. Furthermore RM 794 shows a further variant of the radar equipment of the foretop rangefinder tower: both FuMO 27 and RuMBAnt 7 *Timor* removed and the latter replaced by the large FuMO 24/25 bedspring. Inscription on an official plan (Bundesarchiv RM 25/4-6) indicates that *Tirpitz* carried this configuration between July 1943 and her next refit in spring/summer 1944.

Mr Bullen also has successfully located the passive FuMBAnt 4 *Sumatra* aerials on *Scharnhorst*, *Lützow* and *Admiral Hipper*.

Scharnhorst: Bundesarchiv plans RM 25/5-1 and RM 25/5-11 show them where they should be – on the forward spotting top screen.

Lützow: the *Sumatra* loops can be seen on the front side and the flank of the second level of the armoured spotting top in the picture on page 9, *Warship* 21. See drawing.

Admiral Hipper: the *Sumatra* loops can be detected on the corners of the spotting top screen (IWM pictures CL 2770 and CL 2771; both showing the blasted *Hipper* at Kiel). With this knowledge one can also trace them on the Drüppel photograph RM 542 showing the cruiser about 1942 in Norway. This indicates that *Admiral Hipper* received her passive equipment during her early 1942 refit.

The picture of *Z 39* in *Warship* 22, page 155 shows a lot of interesting electronic equipment. From top to bottom: At the masthead a FuMO 81 *Berlin-S*, on the tiny spur below a FuMBAnt 3 *Bali* and on the next spur below the aerial *Fliege* of the set FuMB 26 *Tunis*. The real nature of the vertical cone on the crossyard, a device that can be found on many pictures, is unclear, it might perhaps be an infra-red detector. The vertical tube between the crossyards, also familiar on most German minor warships, is for protecting and hiding away signal flags. The forward searchlight sponson carries four FuMBAnt 4 *Sumatras*. The active antenna is rather a FuMO 24/25 than a FuMO 21 as stated. The number of passive antennas clearly mirrors the needs of the last year of the war.

The antenna configuration shows that the lefthand destroyer in the picture on page 3, *Warship* 21 is certainly not *Z 39*, as was first assumed.

MAJESTIC PREDREADNOUGHT PT 2 (*Warship* 28)
From Ian Sturton, Southampton, Hants
I have unearthed the accompanying photograph, which might be an 'A & A' to the alteration note at the foot of p281 (Issue 28). It illustrates a 6in Army howitzer specially fitted on the foreturret of *Majestic* or *Prince George* for the beginning of the Dardanelles Campaign, but removed by April 1915.

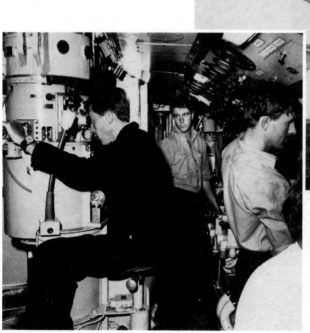
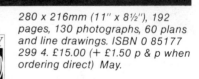

Zeppelin!

A Battle for Air Supremacy in World War I

Ray Rimell

Foreword by Air Marshal Sir Frederick Sowrey

The complete story of the Zeppelin raids over Britain, their devastating effect on the public, the counter-measures and their final defeat is told for the first time in *Zeppelin!* Ray Rimell has spent many years researching the archives, interviewing witnesses and talking to service personnel, both English and German, who actually participated in the battles. The careers of the airships are fully documented and the aircraft and weapons are described in detail, together with the damage they inflicted. Over 300 illustrations – the vast majority of which have never been published – maps and diagrams illustrate the text and there are extensive appendices.

300 x 230mm (12" x 9¼"), 256 pages, 300 illustrations, 15 maps and diagrams. ISBN 0 85177 239 0. £25.00 (+ £2.50 p & p when ordering direct) February.

Available from your local bookseller or by post from

Conway Maritime Press Ltd.

24 Bride Lane, Fleet Street, London EC4Y 8DR

MERCHANT SHIPS AT WAR

The Falklands Experience

Captain Roger Villar DSC RN

The Falklands War is now distant enough to allow an objective appraisal of its achievements and lessons, and this book is the first to study which is probably the most astounding facet of the whole campaign: the rapid requisition, conversion and deployment of a highly varied fleet of nearly 50 merchant ships. Captain Villar meticulously records the details of the modifications and analyses the performance of the merchant fleet in war conditions, using much new information on their activities in the South Atlantic. *Merchant Ships at War* will be widely studied both for the invaluable information on the conversion work, and as a record of the lessons learnt in the first major naval war since 1945.

240 x 184mm (9½" x 7¼"), 192 pages, 135 illustrations. ISBN 0 85177 298 6. £9.50 (+ £1.35 p & p when ordering direct) April.

CONWAY MARITIME

From your local bookshop or by post from
Conway Maritime Press Ltd,
24 Bride Lane, Fleet Street, London EC4Y 8DR